Her plan was clever, but it had backfired.

As the organ played softly in the background and the officiating priest intoned the solemn opening of the nuptial mass, Tara began to tremble.

This was the moment she had waited for; the moment she had rehearsed over and over. The time when, with a glance of disdain, she would turn to her bridegroom and jilt him in front of all his aristocratic friends.

She had ignored her old nanny's warning against her schemes. Now she recognized the full enormity of her sin. But she had left it too late!

Locked in a state of numb, frozen horror, Tara faced the fact that she was incapable of carrying out her plan....

Isle of Calypso

by

MARGARET ROME

Harlequin Books

TORONTO • LONDON • NEW YORK • AMSTERDAM
SYDNEY • HAMBURG • PARIS

Original hardcover edition published in 1979
by Mills & Boon Limited

ISBN 0-373-02264-6

Harlequin edition published June 1979

Printed in U.S.A.

CHAPTER ONE

'TARA O'TOOLE, you're a wicked, wilful girl, and as sure as I am that my name is Bridget McBride I know that if you carry on with this wedding you'll regret it till your dying day! Call it off, child, it's late enough, don't wait until the minute he's ready to slide the ring on to your finger before telling him you've changed your mind!'

'Hmm ...' Coolly, Tara considered, a half-smile teasing her lips. 'But think of the stir it will cause if I wait until the very last minute! I can hardly wait to lead the Most Noble Baron Falcon Falzon up the garden path—or, in this case, up the church aisle—then at a precisely chosen moment to humiliate him before his aristocratic friends by chucking the ring back into his face. Did you know, Bridget,' her smile widened, still musing upon the enjoyable tableau her words had conjured, 'that Maltese nobility are holders of titles recognised by the British Crown, and that if one is to address them correctly one must place the prefix "Most Noble" before each name?' She spun from the window to face her old nanny, green eyes sparkling, her intention to outrage as she deliberated upon Bridget's words, then decided with a show of reluctance, 'Your suggestion is very tempting, but it has one big drawback. *Your* way, the Most Noble

Falcon Falzon's humiliation would be conducted in private, whereas my way everyone on the island who matters will be witness to it. His punishment must be thorough, as painful as that which he inflicted upon Aithne—which is why I mean to see the marriage ceremony through *almost* to its bitter end. Now tell me, how do I look ... ?'

She twirled in front of Bridget, her laughing eyes unmarred by any shadow of conscience, arousing Bridget's ire with the impudent reminder, 'Take a good look, for this is probably the first and last time you'll see me wearing a wedding gown! In,' she snatched a glance at her watch, 'less than an hour from now I shall be entitled to be congratulated upon the success of my mission.'

But Bridget refused to succumb to the charm being projected. 'Not from me, you won't! So far as I'm concerned you're entitled to only one thing —a good spanking—and if you were a few years younger I would——'

Tara's peal of laughter cut through her threat. 'Bridget darlin', you know you wouldn't, because when you had the chance to you never did.'

'More's the pity,' Bridget replied sourly, 'because if I'd delivered a few more spankings I might have two girls to be proud of instead of one whose wild ways are speeding me to my grave and another who's a flibbertigibbet that falls in love with every presentable man she sees and is cast into the depths of despair if her favourite of the month refuses to fall at her feet whenever she flutters her eyelashes. *Aithne!*' she snorted, 'Queen of the Fairies! She is well named, for she walks through life with her feet so far off the ground she's never been known to dash the dew from a buttercup!'

'You misjudge her!' Tara challenged fiercely. 'Aithne is mortal, very much so, and sensitive to pain, especially to the pain of rejection. If you'd seen her as I did ...' Her voice trailed away as, with fists tightly clenched, she relived the memory of her last meeting with her sister, younger by less than a year, but who had always been, and still was, regarded as the baby of the family. Mere weeks ago, looking distraught to the point of hysteria, she had sought out Tara in the grounds of O'Toole's country home and had dropped to her knees to bury her head in her sister's lap.

'Tara,' she had sobbed, 'I feel so miserable, so hurt, and so terribly *used*!' Immediately Tara had suspected a man. As Bridget had implied, Aithne's young life had consisted of a succession of affairs, each one having at its beginning the promise of permanency yet all without exception fizzling into obscurity once Aithne became bored with the idolatry of her latest conquest. This time, however, according to Aithne's heartbroken confidences, some unscrupulous Maltese had taken advantage of her youth and innocence, filled her head with promises he had no intention of fulfilling, then callously turned his back on her when some fresh face had taken his fancy.

Wary of being misled by her sister's well-known penchant for exaggeration, Tara had placed a hand on either side of Aithne's face and levered it firmly upwards until childish blue eyes were forced to meet brilliant green.

'Tell me truthfully,' she had demanded of Aithne, 'exactly how far did you commit yourself to this man?'

To Tara's dismay Aithne had blushed and tried to squirm away. 'Answer me!' she had insisted, emphasising her impatience with a small slap against her sister's cheek. 'Just how foolish have you been?'

The small denim-clad figure had crumpled against her knee as in a trembling whisper she had forced the tearful confession. 'Falcon Falzon is irresistibly attractive, Tara, no warm-blooded woman could refuse any of his demands.'

Bridget stared at her charge, awed by beauty which not even years of familiarity had managed to dim. She had seen Tara dressed for many grand occasions, hunt balls, parties, family celebrations and weddings, each time exquisitely turned out with the aid of an abundance of money, natural good taste, and a flair for choosing shades complimentary to her unusual colouring. But today she looked magnificent. The old woman's slow, uneducated mind sought for adjectives to do justice to the girl whose beauty, in her own homeland, was legendary. Her wedding gown, fashioned from lace hand-woven by the nuns of a nearby convent, hugged a delicious curve of breast, swept inward to stroke across narrow waist and slender thighs, then fell in heavy cream folds to brush against small feet encased in elegant silver sandals.

Her veil was of a deeper shade of cream, mellowed with age, a gossamer-fine web fashioned centuries previously by women of the island who had been noted, even then, for their exquisite artistry. Carefully preserved, it had been worn by generation after generation of Falzon brides. Beneath its demure folds Tara's red hair gleamed like living fire beneath fragile scrollwork. Her body had a quality of stillness that could be unnerving, or peaceful, according to a watcher's mood. A stranger might be forgiven, Bridget thought, as she looked at Tara's bent head and deeply pensive expression, for likening her to an ice maiden, a snow queen, with a coronet of Maltese silver holding her veil firmly in place.

But no woman of ice could lay claim to a ripe, sensuous mouth holding promise of passion, nor to eyes whose brilliance, at first impact, was shocking. A shock that turned to wonder at the discovery of lashes set into place with a sooty finger and fine, dark brows that were her only legacy from her black-haired, happy-go-lucky Irish father.

'If I could have a wish granted on your behalf,' Bridget's whisper was clearly audible in the silent room, 'it would be that you could fall in love.'

Sharply Tara straightened to turn accusing eyes upon her old nanny. 'Please, Bridget, don't start on that tack again, not today!'

'And why not, pray?' Bridget's body quivered with indignation, 'You've had opportunity in plenty, men have courted you in droves—you *and* your sister—but whereas she's fallen for all of them you're never spared a kind word for any. It strikes me you're too keen on arguing. I agree,' she bristled, 'you've needed to keep a wary eye out for fortune-hunters, yet even so, there was no need to scare off all the real men with your caustic tongue.'

'Real men ...?' A derisory laugh began as a gurgle deep in Tara's throat. 'Who are these mythical creatures you keep mumbling about? Describe one to me, outline his virtues, so that if ever I'm fortunate enough to encounter one in real life I'll recognise him immediately!.'

'Mock away, Miss High and Mighty O'Toole!' Bridget hated being laughed at, especially when she could not guess at the source of humour. 'A *real* man,' she plodded on, desperately searching her mind for a description and failing dismally, 'is one who ... who will love and cherish you, who'll be a good husband and a good father to your children—that's most important.'

'A good father ...' Tara kicked the bulk of her skirt behind her and strode towards the window where she stood for a moment in silence. 'Someone like O'Toole, you mean? Is he the one you would have me use as a blueprint in my search for one of your *real* men?'

Bridget's heart plummeted, as she recognised the thread of bitterness running through the sarcastic question. Tara was glaring across the width of the room, daring her to answer, so in an effort to calm her own nerves Bridget began tidying the room, picking up the minutest of threads from the carpet, straightening ornaments that were not awry, using any delaying tactic she thought might divert Tara from demanding an answer.

She should have known her charge better.

'I'm waiting, Bridget?' Tara's foot began tapping an imperious tattoo on the floor. 'Waiting to hear you admit what I've always sworn is true— that the *real* men you talk about are fabrications born of woman's dissatisfaction with her lot—she can't change the pattern of her life once she's married, neither can she change her husband, so she begins to fantasise, to endow her inadequate partner with virtues she *wishes* he possessed, boasting of his virility, exaggerating his worth as a father, his skill as a provider, until eventually the poor dumb fools begins to believe her own publicity!'

Instinctively, Bridget recoiled from such stinging contempt, then softened as she remembered the reason behind her charge's venom.

'My poor love,' she soothed, 'you've dealt with more than your share of men whose main aim in life was to marry money. I sometimes wish you'd been born poor, for money has been more of a curse than a blessing to the O'Toole family—too much money and not enough sense. Your dear mother would have taken her wealth with her to the grave if she had suspected the agony it would cause.'

She sighed, memory bridging the gap between now and the day she had applied for the post of maid to O'Toole's young bride. She had approached the interview without a trace of hope; not many people wished to take into their households a staid, middle-aged spinster and there were other, younger

applicants anxious for the job. But the young bride
had earned Bridget's undying gratitude by recog-
nising loneliness, a need to become involved. Bridget had made sure that she never had cause to regret
her choice. While her young mistress carried her
first baby she waited on her hand and foot, then
when Tara had arrived Bridget had taken over
the duties of the nursery so that her mistress could
recoup her energies to face a second, frighteningly
swift, pregnancy that had proved fatal.

Bridget's gratitude had not died with her mistress; instead, she had lavished love and devotion
upon the two daughters she had left behind, rear-
ing them from infancy until the present day, without help or guidance nor any show of interest from
the man who had made grief his excuse for spending most of his time abroad and loneliness his
explanation for imposing upon his daughters a
succession of stepmothers, not one of whom had
offered a crumb of sympathy when confronted by
his two motherless children.

O'Toole had salved his conscience by showering
the girls with money—a large cheque in place of a
birthday treat, another cheque to excuse his absence
at Christmas, monetary sops to soften the blow of
his non-appearance at school prizegivings, at their
confirmations, and huge expensive hampers of
goodies to prove how concerned he felt whenever
either of them was ill.

Aithne had sailed through her peculiar childhood practically unscathed, and to a stranger's eyes,
so had Tara. Even Bridget was not sure how deeply

her father's indifference had affected the girl, but her simple mind told her, especially at times such as these when she betrayed such intense resentment, that deep down the child felt terribly insecure and distrustful of all members of the opposite sex.

She chanced a look in Tara's direction and was relieved to see her calm. 'I've often wondered who it is you remind me of,' she startled Tara by saying. 'Aithne is your mother's very double, but you're not in the least like her. I know now that it's your maternal grandmother, I can't understand why I didn't realise it sooner.'

'Grandmother Rooney?' Tara smiled. 'I have much to thank her for, she left her entire fortune to me, the darling! Thanks to her generosity I shall be able to live my life in a state of single blessedness, do what I like, when I like, independent even of O'Toole. In just two months' time, when I'm twenty-one, I shall come into my inheritance! I think I'll travel for a while—but first of all I must stay here in Malta for at least a few weeks, just to gloat.'

'Gloat!' If possible, Bridget's black button eyes grew rounder. 'How can you stand there looking like an angel and give voice to such unchristian thoughts? From what little I've seen of Baron Falzon I'd judge him to be a man of strong pride and high principles.'

'Not he!' Tara scoffed. 'Pride he may have, but principles he can't afford, for most of his class are as poor as church mice. The mass of Maltese may be devoutly religious people, but their nobility worship only gold. At this very moment the Baron is probably trying to decide what to buy with my money!' With a second glance at her watch she dismissed her future bridegroom from her mind. 'Shouldn't you be getting dressed for the wedding?' She frowned at Bridget's everyday garments. 'There's not much time left.'

''Tis you who should be dwelling on that fact! You've taken part in many foolhardy escapades during your young lifetime, silly, thoughtless pranks I've put down to high spirits, too much money, and a lack of parental control, but what you plan to do today is devil's work and I'll have no part of it.'

'You mean you're not coming to the wedding?' Tara's cold stare masked her hurt. Neither her sister nor her father had been informed about the wedding because their presence would have been farcical, but the thought of Bridget's stalwart presence in the congregation had been comforting. Suddenly she felt cold and very much alone.

'As you wish.' She turned a stiff back on the tearful old woman whose agitated hands were clasping and unclasping. 'Please go now, I'd like to be alone.'

When the door closed behind her, Tara shrugged off her despondency and strolled across to the window to gaze out at the empty streets below. The room in which she stood was part of the Palazzo Falzon, sited within the M'dina, the Silent City, which in ancient times had been the capital of Malta but which was now all but deserted, its picturesque streets lined with magnificent palaces abandoned by nobles who could no longer afford their upkeep.

It was an uncanny experience walking through the city perched upon a hillside, wondering at the secrets hidden behind honey-coloured stone walls, stepping lightly along muted alleyways where the sound of footsteps was an intrusion upon the brooding silence. Medieval churches and monasteries interspersed the crumbling palaces. As she had wandered the empty streets, puzzled by the absence of people, Tara had been startled at the sight of a bright red Lagonda purring towards her. She had frowned her indignation when the driver had sounded his horn, shattering the silence of centuries with its accursed noise. The driver had pulled up in front of one of the palaces, then strode inside—proof that at least one other was occupied. But during the remainder of her tour the only other sound she had heard was the laughter of children enjoying a short school break and later the soft tones of nuns ushering them back into the convent.

She had realised, after studying dates carved into stone, that the Palazzo Falcon was one of the oldest in existence, and as precedence amongst Maltese nobility was determined not by the degree of the title but by the date of its creation, it would seem to indicate that Baron Falcon Falzon could be regarded as quite a big fish within his small, stagnant pool.

She frowned, disturbed yet unable to fathom why. The task she had set herself had been accomplished with laughable ease. Without Aithne realising it, she had elicited all the information she needed about the playboy Baron, his habits, his favourite places of entertainment, the names of the friends with whom Aithne had stayed while she was on the island and who had been responsible for her introduction to the Baron. Shortly after booking into an hotel she had telephoned Mario and Dolores de Marco, who had been delighted to hear from her and had immediately invited her to join them for dinner that evening.

Looking back, she felt slightly ashamed of the way she had manipulated the likeable couple. Eagerly they had fallen in with her wishes to visit each of the places on her list, and it was at the last one that Dolores had drawn her attention to a couple on the dance floor—tall, dark Baron Falzon paying engrossed attention to his young blonde companion.

Her hiss of satisfaction had had to be disguised as a cough before, in a voice casual to the point of boredom, she had expressed a wish to make his acquaintace. Less than half an hour later her cool fingers had been enclosed in a firm brown clasp and she had been face to face with the man she had sought out expressly to punish. She had studied carefully the man who had broken her sister's heart and in that first instant when their eyes had met she had been overwhelmed by a disturbing sensation which she had refused to recognise as panic.

Dark eyes, falcon-keen; wings of hair, falcon-dark, hugging a proudly arrogant head; a lean face with features sharply etched, and a mouth which, when it was not smiling, fell into a stern line that hinted of a predator's cruelty. Contained within his admiring stare had been qualities inherited from his motley forebears—the boldness of corsairs who had come from the Barbary Coast to raid and plunder, the arrogance of Roman conquerers who had sailed from nearby Sicily, the inscrutability of Arabs whose seal was stamped indelibly upon the island's architecture, the pride of the Knights of Malta from whom the present-day nobility was descended. A smooth rippling of muscles had disturbed an impeccably cut dinner jacket when he had held out a hand to greet her. Seductively, she had smiled into his eyes and had allowed her lips to fall slightly apart to give an impression of being impressed by his attractive presence.

From then onwards their relationship had developed exactly as she had planned. The young blonde had disappeared into the background never to be seen again. For three whole weeks they were together for almost the whole of each day, dancing, swimming, sailing, or just lazing on some secluded beach. The Baron, it seemed, could not see enough of the girl he had christened his green-eyed Irish witch. He fell completely under her spell, which was understandable. Tara, the aloof, could be fascinating; Tara the huntress was devastating!

Without qualm she had played him along, suffering his kisses, pretending to believe his impassioned words of love, allowing him each day some small advance of intimacy until she was sure he was besotted.

Then the time had arrived for the showdown. The Baron's amorous impulses had become almost impossible to control. He was no boy to be deflated by a scolding but a man of the world who, according to Aithne, played Romeo to every Juliet who set foot on his island. One night when they were alone in a secluded garden she had felt the tense line of his jaw beneath her palm; sensed his whipcord body held tightly under control; had been seared by a mouth that captured hers in a kiss that spelt out plainly his desire to possess her; had fought off hands searching for the tiny buttons fastening her bodice, and knew that the time of maximum impact had arrived.

With all her strength she had pushed him away. 'Most Noble Baron,' she had mocked sarcastically, 'prepare yourself for a surprise ...'

The surprise had been hers. With the groan of a man demented he had closed the gap between them to crush her so close she was left in no doubt of his hunger, his virile needs. 'Tara,' he had husked against her parted lips, 'will you marry me?'

For all of a second her brain had been numb, then had begun racing as fast as her heartbeats as she had thought of Aithne, of the girl she herself had usurped, and of the many others who had suffered callous rejection from the bachelor baron. She had not intended to go *quite* so far before jilting him, but ...

'Why not?' she had breathed, awed by her own daring.

His sharp ears had caught the words and had construed them as acceptance. She had not contradicted him.

CHAPTER TWO

CATHEDRAL bells pealed out as, on the arm of the baron's uncle, Tara walked the short distance across the church square, stepping all the time upon flower petals being tossed from baskets held on the arms of pupils from the convent school. Floating in the air was the sound of a choir singing, sweet children's voices swelling louder as they neared the towering entrance to the cathedral whose doors were flung wide as if to embrace the bride.

Feeling no emotion whatsoever, she ascended a flight of shallow steps, honey-coloured stone hollowed by the impression of many feet, flanked either side by two magnificent brass cannons. She hesitated on the threshold, the warmth of sunshine on her back and the forbidding darkness of the interior seeming somehow symbolic. Then, urged forward by a touch at her elbow, she stepped inside to a swell of music from the organ, an anthem of rejoicing from the choir and, at the far end of the aisle, the dark, impatient-looking stranger she was about to jilt.

Every footstep seemed the length of a mile, yet she would not have had her progress shortened by a second. Peeping through the veil covering her face she saw row upon row of the Baron's expensively dressed relatives and smiled to herself, thinking how annoyed they would be to discover that they had squandered money they could ill afford in order to appear affluent at a wedding that was fated to begin and end on the same day.

She glanced upward and found herself staring straight into the eyes of a painted Madonna, not unlike the one Bridget kept at her bedside where she prayed every night and every morning before getting into or out of bed. A spasm of remorse disturbed her features. For some reason thinking about Bridget made her feel guilty. So she pushed all thoughts of her to the back of her mind and concentrated upon heavy silver candlesticks, tall as a man, containing the thickest candles she had ever seen; embroidered altar-cloths; a sculptured crucifix; breathtaking paintings on ceilings and walls, and carvings on wood that looked warmly familiar. Could it *really* be Irish oak? The smell of burning candles was in her nostrils, a smell she always associated with solemn occasions. Why then was she having to fight an insane desire to giggle? As she halted at the foot of the high altar the choir ceased its singing and the notes of the organ faded into silence. She did not turn her head but knew that the Baron had stepped close to her side. As a priest moved down the steps of the altar the Baron's hand rose to pluck aside her veil. Downcast lashes swept upwards to meet his smile, a smile that was pensive but at the same time strained. Suddenly she found it difficult to swallow.

At that moment she recognised the full enormity of her sin! *Bridget had been right, she had left it too late!* As little as half an hour earlier she could have jilted him without a qualm, could indeed have enjoyed the task, seeing herself as an avenging angel sent on behalf of Aithne and the legion of girls who had suffered from the Baron's indifference to the pain he inflicted upon others, to lacerated feelings, to broken hearts.

As the organ began once more to play softly in the background and the officiating priest, flanked on either side by assistant clergy, began to intone the solemn opening of the nuptial mass she began to tremble. She was no stranger to such ceremonies, for Bridget loved weddings and even as children she and Aithne had been dragged along to witness each one that had taken place in their vicinity. Bridget's religious devotion was fanatical, in her opinion a priest was but one step removed from God, and although as Tara had grown older and further removed from the old woman's influence she had become cynical, a trace of the beliefs instilled in childhood still lingered.

The scent of flowers was suffocating; hundreds upon hundreds of them had been used to decorate the church, they were spilling from urns, entwined around the altar rails, massed in dark corners to throw splashes of vivid colour against dark oak carvings and heavily veined marble walls. Panic clawed at Tara's throat when the dignified priest, towering three steps above, resplendent in richly embroidered vestments, indicated that he wanted her and the Baron to kneel. This was the moment she had rehearsed over and over in her mind, the time when with a glance of disdain she would turn to the Baron to address him in tones loud and clear so that everyone would hear: *'Excuse me, Baron, if I leave now. I've decided I don't want to marry you after all.'*

Locked in a state of numb, frozen horror, Tara faced the fact that she was incapable of carrying out her plan. In retrospect, the deed had seemed uncomplicated, but she had reckoned without the atmosphere prevailing, the saintly voices of the children's choir, the eyes of the painted Madonna that seemed to be projecting both sorrow and anger, the devout responses of the congregation and above all, the changed attitude of the Baron, whose stern features indicated that he too was deeply conscious of the utter solemnity of the occasion.

Baroness Falcon Falzon! *The Most Noble Baroness Falzon!* The crowd of well-wishers thronging around the newly wed couple thought it touching the way the bride kept staring with seeming disbelief at the ring on her finger.

'Can't you believe your luck, my dear?' One of the Baron's aunts patted her on the shoulder. 'It is gratifying to know that you are so aware of your good fortune.'

The aunt moved away, unconcerned by the fact that she had received no reply. The girl looked quite stunned, she thought; Falcon's bride, though divinely beautiful, seemed, as yet, overawed by her rise in station.

Tara was indeed overawed, and speechless, and stunned by the extent of her own folly. Once outside the cathedral normal reactions had taken over. The inertia that had gripped her had faded and in its place had come shock, shock at her own stupidity, amazement that she could have allowed the marriage to take place, confusion as to how she could go about wiping out the wrong.

The Baron, however, was in sparkling form, looking everyone's idea of a delighted bridegroom. During a momentary lull when for a second everyone's attention was diverted away from them, he whispered in her ear, 'I'm pleased that the colour has returned to your cheeks, I know it is not expected to see desire in the eyes of a bride, but did you have to look quite so petrified?'

'Baron ...' she began impulsively, then when his eyebrows winged, amended with haste, 'Falcon, I must speak to you alone.'

'Now?' His eyes swept the assembled guests. 'Can't you wait until later?'

'No, I can't!' she hissed, desperate to put an end to the whole farcical situation.

Frowning, he set down his glass of champagne. They were standing together in the main hall of the Palazzo greeting guests as they arrived, but the last of them had been shown into the dining-room and were even now being seated along massive lengths of table with, reflected upon a mirror-bright surface, flowers spilling from crystal vases, tablemats of priceless lace, red and white napkins each folded into the shape of a rose, silver tureens piled high with fruit, bottles of champagne steeped up to their necks in ice, and antique cutlery stamped with the arms of the House of Falzon.

'I'm afraid you will have to,' Falcon's voice was puzzled yet firm, 'our guests are waiting for us to join them.'

For a nightmarish two hours Tara endured the monotony of toying with food she could not stomach, conversation which she only half grasped, interminable speeches from Falcon's male relatives, each of whom seemed to be trying to outdo the other in verbosity. But at last, when every possible toast had been drunk, guests began retiring from the table to regroup in the huge main hall to chat and sip champagne.

Deciding they need wait no longer, Tara began, 'Falcon ...!'

Immediately his dark head swung towards her. 'Yes, my darling?' His eyes roved her pale features, showing a hunger that was intense. Instinctively she recoiled, but he seemed unaware of her aversion as he looked deeply into her eyes and murmured, 'I think we have done our duty, we can now get ready to leave.'

'Leave?' she enquired, her green eyes open wide.

'On our honeymoon,' he reminded her gently. 'Have you forgotten that we agreed to spend it on my estate in Gozo? Though it's just a few miles from the mainland, you'll find the island much quieter, much less densely populated than Malta. There we will find the seclusion we need.'

She had not forgotten; the information, whenever he had given it, simply had not registered. Most of what he had said to her over the past three weeks had gone right over her head; obviously she must have smiled and nodded in all the right places, but her own thoughts had occupied her mind to such an extent that she was not aware of half he had said.

Side by side they took leave of their guests, all the time making towards the flight of stairs leading upwards to the floor above. Tara's relief upon reaching the peace of a quiet passageway was shortlived when, with the impatience of a man who has fought too long with frustration, he pulled her hard up against him and with a groan covered her mouth with his. He had kissed her before, many times, but not in this way which was like the branding of a possession, like the stamping of a hot seal of ownership upon a parcel proclaiming: 'This is mine!'

Resentment shot through every nerve, setting alight the touch paper of a temper which during the past weeks she had striven hard to control. Furiously she wrenched her mouth from his and was just about to deliver a tirade of abuse when a nearby door opened and Bridget stepped out into the passageway.

'So there you are!' Both her voice and her expression echoed great satisfaction. 'I've laid out your going-away outfit on the bed, Baroness,' she dropped a mock curtsey, 'and packed everything I thought you'd need for your honeymoon.'

Falcon muttered an imprecation under his breath and stepped back, but the smile he directed at Bridget was full of charm. To her great delight, he bent to place a light kiss upon her withered cheek. 'A small thank-you for looking after my wife so well;

she is lucky to have such a devoted friend.'

Tara knew as soon as she saw it happen that Bridget would be completely bowled over; she had known few men in her lifetime, none of them intimately. She cringed at the thought of what was now in store, in common with most simple, plain women, Bridget was a sucker for rogues. With one kiss Baron Falzon had pinched her only ally.

Her fears were confirmed when Bridget coloured fiercely and stammered, 'I agree that Tara is a lucky girl—lucky to have a husband such as yourself.'

He turned his attention back to Tara, noting that the sparkle had returned to her eyes but far from guessing the reason why. 'I'll allow you fifteen minutes to change, and not a second longer. Wear something warm, my darling, although the sun is still high it will be fading by the time we reach the coast, and we are making the crossing to Gozo by speedboat.'

As Tara flounced inside the bedroom Bridget followed wearing a smirk that was infuriating. Angry with herself, Tara vented her spleen on the old woman, who was so used to her tantrums she paid them little attention.

'How can you *smarm* so to that odious man! Have you no sense of loyalty towards Aithne?' Quite unperturbed, Bridget began helping her dispose of the veil.

'I think this is the happiest day of my life,' she smiled, ignoring Tara's jibe. 'To see you married at last—and to such a man!'

Furiously, Tara shrugged away. 'You said you

wouldn't be attending the wedding.'

'I couldn't keep away,' Bridget admitted, 'I was drawn to the cathedral against my will. I couldn't believe you capable of carrying out such a plan, and my faith was justified. I've tried hard to bring up you two girls in the way your mother would have wished and over the years I've grown more and more disheartened, wondering where I'd gone wrong. When you told me what you intended doing to the Baron I felt certain I'd failed in my duty, both to yourself and to your mother, but then,' she beamed, 'as the ceremony progressed and I heard your responses, saw the ring sliding on to your finger, I knew that at heart you were a good, God-fearing child. You've married a *real* man, Tara ...' She hesitated and bit her lip when her charge threw her a look of bitter scorn. 'In my opinion he's exactly the sort of husband you need.'

'An opinion formed less than five minutes ago with the help of a kiss on the cheek!' Tara rounded, enraged and hurt by Bridget's shift of allegiance. 'And as for his making me a good husband,' she stormed, 'not even you could be stupid enough to imagine that I intend to remain married to him one moment longer than necessary!'

Bridget looked blank. 'Those whom God hath joined together ...' she faltered.

'A good fat cheque can tear asunder!' Tara cut in. Savagely, she clawed the dress from her body and flung it into a far corner of the room. 'I've been insanely foolish, I'll admit, but thanks to Grandmother Rooney I can afford to bribe the Baron into giving me a divorce.'

'Divorce?' Bridget tasted the word and found it sour. 'He will never agree to that; divorce is as rare in his country as it is in ours.'

'An annulment, then.' Tara glared. 'Anything will suffice if it rids me of the Baron.'

For some reason unknown to Tara Bridget's shocked look gave way to one of complacancy. 'You seem very confident of getting your own way,' she stooped to pick up Tara's discarded clothes. 'Personally, I think you might find that the Baron's views on that subject are very different from your own.' Refusing to become ruffled, she continued to ignore Tara's glare and questioned, 'Now, which outfit are you going to wear?' At the threat of a sharp protest she raised her hand in an imperious manner so reminiscent of the way she had quelled rebellion in the nursery that Tara immediately fell silent. 'According to the Baron, Gozo is small and sparsely inhabited, if you intend to fight him then wait until you get there. The fewer people around the better when flint strikes stone.'

Soberly, Tara conceded the wisdom of this remark and began dressing for the trip across the short stretch of sea separating the islands. Bridget was not always wrong; she had said that the Baron had pride. She could be right. To injure that pride before a houseful of his relatives would be foolish; far better to allow him to return alone to Malta giving, if he wished, an impression of having tired of his bride rather than arouse the curiosity of gossips by packing her bags and leaving the Palazzo on the very day of the wedding.

So with less than five minutes to spare she threw on a sweater and slacks, shrugged into a lightweight anorak of bright green and was just attempting to bundle her mass of bright hair beneath a matching peaked cap when, without warning, the Baron strode into the room. He too was casually but elegantly dressed in a jacket and slacks of matching denim teamed with a black polo-necked sweater. The room seemed to shrink as he strode towards her, his tread noiseless, body movements fluid, keen eyes searching. All the characteristics, she thought with a shiver, of an animal about to pounce.

She tensed when his hands clasped her shoulders, then stroked caressingly down the length of her arms to clasp her hands in his. Quizzically, he eyed her outfit, an amused smile quirking his lips.

'What a transformation!' he teased lightly, then called across his shoulder, 'What have you done with my delectable bride, Bridget, have you spirited her away and left an urchin in her place?'

'You'll have to get used to that,' Bridget's answering chuckle was slightly grim, 'she matches her mood to her dress and changes it just as often. In a swimsuit she's Tarzan's mate; in a tennis outfit, Virginia Wade; in a riding habit, Lucinda Prior Palmer. I can't tell you how terrified I felt when I saw her dressed for her first lesson in piloting a plane!'

With eyes alight with laughter he bent to place

his lips against Tara's ear and murmured, 'I can hardly wait to discover whom you will emulate when you wear no clothes at all!'

Her cheeks were still flaming when he handed her into a powerful sports car—one of the few expensive cars she had seen on the island—then slid behind the wheel to begin the short journey to the coast.

The sun was sinking slowly behind them as he nosed the car through the huge stone archway which was the point of entry or exit from the Silent City, and set off along roads running easterly through the heart of the island towards the coast. As Tara relaxed in her seat he did not intrude upon her enjoyment of the drive with conversation, leaving her to examine the unfamiliar landscape of small patchwork fields that looked parched compared with the green of her homeland. But to compensate for the lack of lush vegetation was cloudless sky, glimpses of deep blue sea, blossoms pushing their way through cracks in walls, flourishing along the sides of dusty roads, massed in every kind of container and set on steps and balconies of villas built of golden stone, arched and pillared, Arabian fashion, to capture every hint of breeze.

Now and again he pointed out a vineyard; a herd of grazing goats; a wayside shrine, in fact, anything he thought might be of interest to her. But mainly he remained silent, speeding along the roads as if eager to achieve the reward he was convinced lay at the end of their journey.

She did not want to disabuse him—yet. Although

once she was tempted, when with a squeal of brakes he drew up, stepped out of the car, and walked a few paces back towards a stand that had been set up at the side of the road. When he returned he tossed a paper bag into her lap.

'*Figolli*,' he explained, 'sweetmeats made in the shape of lambs, doves, or birds, animals that represent purity and freedom from the vices of the world. If there had been time,' he grinned, 'I might have asked to have one made in the image of my bride.'

'You consider me to be pure and free of vices?'

'Not entirely free of vices.' As he slipped into gear he slanted a wicked look. 'I have glimpsed temper and a hint of obstinacy. But pure you most certainly are.'

'How can you be so certain?' She shot up straight, indignant at being made to feel somehow naïve.

'Because I have sensed your fear of men,' he informed her calmly, keeping his attention upon the road. 'In a dozen ways a woman subconsciously betrays innocence. '

'How?' she had to know.

She hated his smile of patronage, the negligent manner in which he searched for a cheroot, then set its tip upon a lighter he took from the dashboard. She simmered as he skilfully guided the car around twists and bends before, with earthy, brutal honesty, tearing her equilibrium to shreds.

'In the initial stages of a relationship a man has to pick his way carefully before deciding whether his companion is a woman of experience or a virgin.

Many virgins attempt to appear experienced, you understand, but as the affair progresses signs become evident to any man of perception—the gasp deep within the throat when she is surprised by seeking lips; the alarmed arching of a spine feeling for the first time a man's fingers fumbling with the fastenings of her dress; the quiver of a breast previously untouched; the stiffening of a body held close and hard enough to absorb the extent and knowledge of a man's virility.'

The tips of her ears felt red hot. 'You sensed all that in me?' She rushed on, not really wanting to know. 'Couldn't those signs also indicate frigidity?'

'They could,' he agreed carelessly, 'were it not that within the bundle of contradiction that is woman there are later signals that cancel out the first.' His tone deepened to a husk as he assured her, 'I have no qualms about your capacity for loving, witch bride. Though your passion may be a secret hidden even from yourself I have felt response in lips quivering beneath mine; my ears have quickened to moans of ecstasy that yours have probably missed; I have felt the involuntary thrust of your breast against my body, the pressure of hungry thighs.'

'You most certainly have not!'

In her bright green anorak and peaked cap she reminded him of a small indignant pixie when he glanced her way, and he burst out laughing. Pulling up the car at the side of a jetty where a speedboat was bobbing on top of the water, he grinned down into her outraged face and pleaded, 'Don't waste precious time arguing, pixie bride! After all, there is a lifetime ahead of us if you wish to prove me wrong.'

CHAPTER THREE

IN direct contrast to the flat, parched island they had left behind, Gozo was hilly and green. Tara glimpsed a ferryboat disgorging people and cars on to the quayside of a small but busy harbour before the boat swept in an arc around the headland where cliffs fell steeply into aquamarine water, fathoms deep, yet clean and pure enough to mirror a fascinating world of coloured rocks, writhing fronds of marine plants and shoals of small fish darting, gliding shadow-dark, then, as if at a given signal, changing direction *en masse*.

The boat sped along a coast rich in caves and grottoes, magnificent cliffs topped by crumbling towers, olive groves, a few grazing sheep and goats, but no people. By the time Falcon began nosing the boat into a small cove to head towards a wooden jetty Tara was feeling a sense of exile, a certainty that here she could become swallowed up by solitude, deserted and forgotten by the outside world.

'Welcome to Gozo!' With a smile she distrusted he helped her ashore, then with his hand upon her elbow began guiding her along a gently sloping path leading upwards to a house perched upon a hillside, its oriental outline bathed blood red by the rays of the setting sun.

The house, she thought, typified that side of the

man's nature that clung to the traditions of his bizarre forebears, a house built for an Arab grandee where, hidden within its silent depths, might be housed the quarters of a secret harem. They entered through a classical archway bearing the arms of the House of Falzon, then stepped through a gateway cut out of an ironwork screen, intricately scrolled to give an impression of delicacy yet unable, because of its impassive rigidity, to disguise the fact that its initial purpose had been to restrict captives and to discourage intrusion by strangers.

The interior was made up of large rooms, some windowless, some doorless, that opened on to galleries running around three sides of a courtyard. Palm trees waved their fronds above the roof of the two-storey building and cast shade upon gardens bursting with exuberant blossoms. A fountain had a centrepiece of twin dolphins spouting water from their mouths into a basin lined with colourful tiles and around the main patio were archways, their fretwork outstanding like rows of jagged teeth against the darkening night sky. Inside, walls were lined from floor to ceiling with vividly patterned azulejo tiles—a house designed for leisurely movement from one room to another while seeking refuge from the sun in the depths of cold shadow, a wisp of breeze, the relief of exchanging one cool surface for another.

'Well,' Falcon's voice stroked past her ear, 'does our honeymoon retreat meet with your approval?'

Tara swallowed hard to disperse a nervous lump in her throat; her bravado had fled the moment she set foot inside the house that held an ambience evocative of Eastern mystique, slave girls, harems, and the totally dominant male.

She was saved the effort of a reply by the appearance of a manservant padding soft-footed towards them. With a sigh of exasperation for yet another interrupted moment of intimacy, Falcon acknowledged his presence.

'Paul, this is your new mistress, the Baroness Falzon.'

If the dark, inscrutable Maltese noticed her wince of distaste at the mention of her new title he made no sign. The muscles at each corner of his mouth twitched into an apology for a smile as he inclined his head in her direction before stooping to pick up the luggage. 'Inform your good wife, Maria,' the Baron continued easily as they mounted the stairs in Paul's wake, 'that I shall expect to see some of our island's traditional dishes served at dinner this evento tempt the appetite of my bride. Some *Bragioli*, perhaps, or *Torta tal-Lampuki* ...'

Paul deposited their luggage at the foot of a bed draped in a cover of hand-woven lace. 'In Gozo lies the heart of the lace-making industry,' Falcon told her, following her eyes as they traced a pattern of lovers' knots, winged cupids and twin hearts woven into one.

The lovers' theme was continued in drapes hung at huge windows stretching from ceiling to floor and in the velvet-textured carpet, dove-grey, except in each corner where lovebirds were entwined in a perpetual state of amorous bliss. Even the coffering of the ceiling repeated the seductive theme, displaying sheaves of wheat and eggs with half-opened shells, the symbols of fertility.

'The bridal suite,' he pointed out unnecessarily, then frowning at her lack of response, he dismissed Paul, who was preparing to unpack their luggage. 'Leave that until later. When the Baroness has rested for a couple of hours you may serve dinner.'

In an attempt to appear as nonchalant as possible Tara walked across to a wardrobe lining the whole of one wall. The sweet smell of cedarwood drifted out of its depths as she slid open the door and reached for one of the silk-padded hangers lining the rail. Her vivid green anorak looked incongruous in such alien surroundings—as incongruous as she felt herself in this house with the atmosphere of a Moorish palace. She braced when he spoke behind her, very close, yet resisting the impulse to touch.

'What's wrong, Tara?' he asked gravely. 'Bridal nerves are to be expected, but you seem almost ... afraid.'

At last the moment of truth had arrived! With a courage typical of her breeding she did not shirk the issue. Slowly she turned round to face him and with green eyes brilliant in a small, white face, offered the distinct reply, *'I am Aithne's sister!'*

Not unexpectedly, he was a past master at the art of simulating surprise; even she, who was aware of all the facts, suffered a momentary twinge of doubt when his brows formed two questioning arcs above eyes that were dark mirrors of puzzlement.

'You have a sister? You have made no previous

reference to her—why wasn't she present at our wedding?'

The dam of her temper burst, sweeping caution away on a raging torrent of anger. 'You know very well why! It was she who ought to have been your bride, she whom you tricked and degraded, then tossed aside when your fickle fancy settled upon another. *How dare you*,' she stamped her foot with rage, 'pretend to know nothing of my sister!'

His dark head jerked from the impact of eyes glaring emerald green, from the look of hatred which was the last thing he had expected from the bride whose subdued silence had aroused his concern.

'You're a *beast*!' she lashed him, 'an unscrupulous, poverty-ridden gigolo who flits from one woman to the next, your measure of affection coinciding exactly with the size of her bank balance!'

The insult lit flames in the depths of eyes staring with shocked amazement at his virago wife. His lean form recoiled, then recovered with such swiftness that she was unprepared when he pounced, digging clawed fingers of steel into the soft flesh of her shoulders.

'Tell me one thing,' he hissed through lips set in a mask of grim disbelief, 'why did you marry me?'

'To pay you back in your own coin,' she panted, determined not to betray panic, 'to make you regret ever having met, much less ill-treated, an O'Toole! The marriage was a mistake, my intention was to jilt you, to walk out on you in the middle of the

ceremony, baring your humiliation to the world—
or at least, to all the world that you care about—but
at the last minute I discovered I was incapable of
sinking to your level. However, it's a mistake that
can easily be rectified.' Angrily she pulled away
from a grasp that had become lifeless and with a
toss of her fiery head marched across to the bed
where her handbag was, lying. Furiously she rum-
maged, then withdrew her hand to flourish a cheque
book. 'Name your price!' she demanded crudely.
'How much do you require to arrange a quick
divorce?'

Her words did not have the required reaction.
Indeed, he seemed almost not to have heard as he
stared long and deeply at the face of the girl whom
just a few hours previously he had vowed to love and
to cherish. He shook his head as if to free himself
of some nightmare, then walked slowly across the
width of the carpet until only a few inches separated
them. A more gullible person might have been
fooled by the grave sincerity in his voice when
slowly he spelled out:

'Please believe that I am speaking the truth, Tara,
when I swear that I have no recollection whatsoever
of this sister you speak of, cannot recall even the
mention of her name—a name so unusual it would
be almost impossible to forget. When and where am
I supposed to have met her? And more important,
of what, exactly, am I being accused?'

Tara reacted like a tigress protecting her young.
If he was speaking the truth it would mean that
Aithne had lied, and that was not possible—she was

capable of a white lie, perhaps, a prevarication even, but not a damning indictment of a man's character simply to vent petty spite. No, Aithne's distress had been too genuine to have been founded on lies.

She tossed her head so that he caught the full blast of stormy eyes. 'It was in Malta, mere weeks ago, that you met my sister, seduced her, then callously cast her aside! Do you wonder that I sought you out deliberately to seek revenge? Jilting is too good for you—you ought to be——'

'Oh, Tara!' To her astonishment she saw that he was laughing, eyes alight with amusement, his body incredibly relaxed. 'I suspected I might be the victim of mistaken identity, and your words have proved me right! Not even if I were the stud you so obviously think I am, could I forget any woman who had loomed so largely in my life?' He stepped closer until his lips were a mere fraction from hers, and whispered, 'Come, pixie bride, this is supposed to be our honeymoon, don't you think we have wasted enough time discussing people of no consequence?'

She sprang out of reach. 'Don't you dare touch me!' she ordered coldly, then, waving the cheque book under his nose, she demanded, 'I'm waiting to learn the price of my freedom.'

He jerked away as if struck, the sense of her message registering only at the second time of hearing. Pride hardened his features, the pride of a man who demanded complete trust, utter loyalty, from the woman he had chosen to be his wife.

'Divorce is out of the question,' he clamped, 'no

matter how much you are prepared to pay.'

'Annulment, then!' she insisted, goaded by an irrational fear.

'Nor that either!' The words crackled like ice on his lips. 'The main requirement for an annulment is that the marriage should not be consummated—a circumstance that will certainly not apply in our case.'

It was bluff, of course, she told herself long after the door had closed behind him, the sort of bluff that might have scared a less spirited girl but one that cut no ice with someone who was his equal and in some respects his better. After all, she was an heiress and, as she had discovered very early in life, money talked loud and clearly; money, providing the amount was large enough, could solve every problem. And as for breeding—was she not the eldest daughter of O'Toole, chief of one of the oldest clans in Ireland?

To occupy hands that were strangely agitated, she began unpacking her luggage and discovered much to her exasperation that Bridget had packed the very last things that she herself would have chosen. She liked functional clothes, well-cut slacks, comfortably casual separates and, if a dress should be absolutely necessary, something plain and uncluttered. She had brought a vast amount of clothes to Malta, frivolous, tantalising, sophisticated items that had been chosen especially to aid her planned assault upon the senses of the amorous Baron whose penchant for alluring women was well known.

Now that her mission had been accomplished she

would have banished to the back of her wardrobe
every one of the items that obstinate, sentimental
Bridget had included in her luggage. With disgust
she eyed every article she unpacked, slinky cat-suits
which she loathed, low-cut evening gowns of organ-
die, frilled and flounced around neckline and hem;
dresses designed to be worn off the shoulder, with
full skirts and an annoying amount of fashionable
frilled petticoat showing beneath the hem. As she
withdrew the last minute articles from the suitcase
her breath caught in a gasp of outrage. *'Bridget, you
old hypocrite!'* she muttered, glaring down at wisps
of cotton dangling between her fingers—micro-
scopic bikinis which only last week Bridget had
vociferously condemned as outrageous but which
seemingly could be considered respectable now that
she had achieved marital status!

With a mutter of exasperation, she snapped shut
the lock of her suitcase and bundled it out of sight.

She was conscious of gnawing hunger and thought
with longing of the breakfast she had refused to
touch that morning and of the sumptuous lunch
that had been left untasted on her plate. There
was nothing else for it but to join the Baron for
dinner. Much as she would have liked to forgo the
doubtful pleasure, an hour in his company was
preferable to a night rendered sleepless by hunger
pangs. Her mind made up, she sauntered back to
the wardrobe, confident that whatever she chose to
wear would be hardly likely to arouse the interest of
her disenchanted bridegroom.

An hour later, showered, refreshed, and feeling

much more confident, she twirled in front of a
mirror to examine the effect of a black, ankle-length
dress fashioned from soft jersey, simple in shape,
yet lending to her slight figure an air of sophisti-
cation. She frowned, not quite satisfied. The figure-
hugging material made poetry of uptilted breasts,
deeply incurving waist and a perfect flow of hipline.
Creamy shoulders were bared by a bodice cut just
low enough to reveal an eye-riveting valley of
shadow between her breasts. Her flaming hair was
a startling contrast to the starkness of her dress, yet
she felt that the overall effect was too subdued. As
inspiration struck she snapped her fingers and
twirled towards a drawer. Quickly she searched,
then withdrew a deeply-fringed shawl which she
swathed around her waist, then tied, gypsy fashion,
over one hip. From a vase of flowers she chose a deep
red rose which she tucked securely into the knot,
then stood back satisfied to once more examine her
image which, with the help of a few subtle touches,
had been transformed from the subdued to the flam-
boyant.

The Baron did not appear to escort her downstairs but sent Paul to tell her that dinner was ready
to be served. Feeling much more relaxed than she
had felt all day, Tara descended the staircase which
climbed in large tiled squares from a gloomy well
up to a high semi-domed ceiling now shrouded in
shadow. Paul was waiting at the foot of the stairs
to escort her into a small, comfortably furnished
room that she had not previously noticed. When
he announced her presence, Falcon turned from

the table at which he was pouring drinks, and greeted her gravely.

'I am pleased that you have decided to join me for dinner. Your appearance is proof of a certain maturity—I abominate women who sulk.'

Gracefully, she accepted the glass of wine he proffered, being careful not to make contact with a brown hand wearing on one finger a heavy gold ring bearing the crest of the House of Falzon. She sipped, then nodded her approval. 'Mmm ... delicious!'

'For a bad night, a mattress of wine,' he quoted lightly, holding her gaze, daring her to look away.

When she could bear his scrutiny no longer she laid down her glass and swung away, projecting bravado by adopting a deliberately provocative, hip-swinging walk as she put space between them. Her palms were sweating slightly, however, when she sank into an armchair and tried to look unconcerned. A task made almost impossible when his gaze shifted to primly-crossed ankles made to look incredibly slender by the encircling diamanté straps of her evening shoes.

'As yet,' he spoke as if his mind were on other things, 'our local wines do not have the acclaim they deserve, even though our wine-producing industry is one that dates back into the distant past. Long before the Greeks and Romans came to our islands, early settlers discovered, in the happy coincidence of soil and sunshine, that our climate was ideal for the growing of the grape. Today we have a vastly increased acreage devoted to vineyards and the industry enjoys all the added advantages of the latest technical know-how. All that is lacking is sufficient publicity—a situation which I intend, very shortly, to remedy.'

Tara's lashes flew up over incredulous eyes. '*You* intend to remedy?' The inflection could not have been more insulting.

As punishment, he shifted his gaze, allowing it to linger upon the deep plunge of shadow between her breasts, then he confounded her further with the casual admission:

'Certainly. The House of Falzon is foremost among the wine producers of Malta and I pride myself that my company, though long established, is one that moves with the times.'

Provided with fresh food for thought, she barely tasted what she ate, though was not remiss enough to forget to ask Paul to compliment his wife on the excellence of the meal that had been eaten in almost complete silence. It was with a great feeling of relief that she drained her coffee cup and stood up to take her leave of the brooding Baron, who rose politely to his feet and made no move to detain her when, with more haste than elegance, she retreated from the room, despising her own timidity in not pressing the subject that was uppermost in her mind, for allowing his silent immobility to unnerve her to such a degree that she had been actually afraid to broach once more the subject of divorce.

Once inside her bedroom she undressed and slipped between silken sheets, her sleepy eyes tracing the antics of winged cupids, soaring, drifting, seeming almost alive as a breeze from the open window teased the delicate drapes. For a while she mulled over the surprising fact that the House of Falzon was not bankrupt as she had imagined, then, giving in to overwhelming drowsiness, she allowed heavy eyelids to fall and dismissed the Falzon winery as a worthless toy, probably used by the Baron as a front to disguise his idleness.

She was almost asleep when a sound disturbed the silence. With an effort she raised a lazy eyelid, then jerked wide-awake at the sight of a shadow advancing towards her. Fear paralysed her throat as the shadow took form and she saw broad shoulders shrug out of a dressing-gown, heard the whisper of silk as it fell to the floor.

Without uttering a word he threw back the covers and slid into bed beside her. It was not until she felt the cool shock of his flesh against hers that she began to fight, soundlessly, desperately, raking sharp fingernails deeply into his shoulders as the weight of his body pinned her firmly down.

For what seemed eternity she fought him, tossing her head from side to side to avoid the mouth that was stifling the screams in her throat. When tears ran down her cheeks he kissed them away, as her struggles grew weaker he soothed the body quivering beneath him with soothing strokes, tender yet ever dominant.

Utterly exhausted, her hair a mess of damp tendrils clinging to her head, she finally lapsed quiescent in his arms, and it was then that he began to make love to her, sweet, tender love that aroused a dull, yearning ache in her virgin body, an ache more potent than pain, a yearning more savage than the temper he had tamed. His mouth was a brand upon her lips, demanding, bruising, rousing. His hands seared, exploring every secret part of her.

She became too weak to resist, too shocked to pull rein on stampeding senses. Strange, unfamiliar emotions strengthened, overriding her will, until somehow, at some unidentifiable moment she began to respond, grew warm and sensuous in his arms, sipped her first taste of passion, found it addictive as a drug, and was devoured by it ...

CHAPTER FOUR

THE sun had not been long risen, so as Tara cleaved the waters of the pool, lined with green tiles to give an impression of coolness on even the hottest day, the water swilled cold against her feverish body. It could do nothing, however, to soothe the furore of a mind tortured by regret, dismay, and utter disbelief.

She rolled on her back, exhausted, and with eyes closed against the pierce of a strengthening sun began floating on top of the water. For almost an hour she had raced the length of the pool, backward and forward in an effort to outpace her racing thoughts, but in no way could she dismiss the disastrous fact that as dawn had broken she had wakened with a start, feeling arms holding her protectively, even in sleep, and to the horrible realisation that she had spent a long, passionate night in the arms of a man she hated.

A tremor of distaste disturbed the mask of calm she was trying so hard to retain. Incidents had occurred during the night which she did not dare examine too closely, moments so incredibly magical they would not bear daylight scrutiny. He was a devil, a sorcerer! How else could he have sublimated her will to such an extent that each time during the night when he had reached out for her—

and there had been many—she had responded with the eagerness of a wanton. There had even been one occasion when *she* had wakened *him* with a kiss ... !

A sob racked her body. Unable to bear another moment of self-torture, she rolled over and struck out for the side. Her intention was to hide, to seek some solitary place where, in the manner of a maimed animal, she could curl up small and lick her wounds. But as she hauled her dripping body up the steps at the side of the swimming pool a shadow fell across her face. She looked up and saw Falcon, his lithe body bare except for swim trunks smooth and sleek as a second skin. Tall, dark and bronzed, he laughed down at her, a magnificent sun-god expecting worship.

She averted her eyes, pretending not to see the helping hand he extended, and snatched the robe she had left at the side of the pool, belting it tightly around her waist, subconsciously emulating the caution of a victim who, having once been robbed, is determined to protect what little is left. Weakness shot through her body when behind her he teased tenderly:

'Are you the nymph, Calypso, returned to her island? It was here on Gozo that she was said to have lived, here that she offered her lover Ulysses immortality if he stayed with her for ever. Legend has it that Calypso's charm was so great it was seven years before he could bear to tear himself away.'

'And you see yourself as Ulysses?' The question grated past her lips. 'The comparison is apt. Did not Homer represent him as being full of artifices?'

Her back was turned towards him, yet tingling nerves gave warning that he had stepped close, so close that his voice jarred against her ear.

'Do you mean to continue with this pretence of dislike? Even after last night ...' the birds seemed to cease singing during the sharp pause, '... will you try to deny that we are a complete and perfect whole?' Suddenly he urged, 'Our love is a tender exotic seedling, Tara! Allow it to flourish and grow strong, don't trample it beneath the heel of obstinacy!'

Shaken and angered by the effect of his words, she rounded to attack. Green eyes stormed over his face, unheeding of its grimness, seeing only a rakish mouth, a taunting devil's eyes. Our *love*, as you call it, is a weed, a poisonous, choking weed that appeared where it was not wanted so must be uprooted as swiftly as possible before it defiles healthy soil. Like all evils, it is quick to spread and hard to destroy. But I *will* have it destroyed!' Her agitation grew wild. 'I *will* have a divorce!'

Falcon had been prepared to reason, to soothe his distraught bride whose anger had its basis in bewilderment, the bewilderment of a child made suddenly aware that she is possessed of a mature and hungry body. But he was a man born to be proud and her scorn was great. He resisted the urge to touch her, knowing she was still a stranger to the passion, newly-discovered, that was as tempestuous as her temper. She needed time to come to terms with the new awareness of her body, time to learn that passion was a gift not all of her sex were blessed with, a possession to be regarded not with shame but with thankfulness.

He wanted to kiss her into submission, but instead folded his arms across his chest, hiding tightly-clenched knuckles out of sight.

'Don't goad me too far, tiger bride,' he menaced softly. 'Till death us do part is no platitude to be mouthed without meaning, but a solemn vow which I intend shall be kept. Like it or not, resigned or unresigned, your nights will be spent in my arms, your days by my side.' Moved to compassion by her stricken look, he continued softly, 'What I did last night was not easy, Tara. I would have much preferred a willing bride, but you left me no choice but to fight for what was mine. Does the fighting have to continue? Can't you be generous and admit defeat, be courageous and admit to ... love?'

Bitterly she replied, 'You'll receive only one virtue from me—the virtue of honesty. I hate you, Baron Falzon, and if you insist upon refusing me my freedom I'll do everything in my power to make you change your mind.'

'So be it.' His reply was terse, an acceptance of her insistence upon declaring war. 'Some of the blame must be mine, for hate is a consequence of fear. There is one consoling factor,' he tossed across his shoulder before diving into the pool, 'you feel for me the strongest emotion of all. Love can turn to indifference, even disgust—hatred alone is immortal.'

He did not expect her to reply so did not turn

his head to see her staring, stricken with shame, at weals outstanding, red, angry, claw-deep, across the breadth of his shoulders. She looked down at her fingernails, expecting to see them dripping with his blood, then with a shiver of revulsion she spun round and ran into the house, questioning frantically the effect he had upon her emotions, wondering why, when she wanted so badly to remain cool, he was able to arouse within her the reactions of a savage.

She spent the rest of the day in her room, refusing all offers of food and drink, whiling away the hours reading or just sitting by the window staring into solitary gardens, searching an empty sky for inspiration that might guide her out of the mess wrought by her own criminal folly. As the sun began to set, shrouding the woven cupids, the hearts, the embracing lovebirds in intimate shadow, panic stirred at the reminder that night-time was the time lovers preferred.

Her heart was thumping as she ran across to the door, then began to race at the discovery that there was no lock, no protective bolt to ram home. She dragged a stool in front of the double doors and sat down, aware that her slight weight would be no barrier to a marauding man yet determined not to give in without a struggle. For hours she sat immobile, her eyelids growing heavier, her drooping head jerking erect at every suspicion of sound. Dawn was breaking by the time she crawled into bed, satisfied that Falcon was not coming yet incensed by the suffering his absence had caused.

Common sense told her, when she awoke unre-
freshed and heavy-eyed, that she could not skulk
inside her room for ever. Reluctantly she dressed
and went down to breakfast, hoping the bright
buttercup yellow of her dress would distract attention from the dark circles beneath her eyes. It was
a vain hope.

Falcon had finished breakfast and was enjoying
a last cup of coffee while he read his newspaper. His
head lifted as she approached; he narrowed his eyes
against the sun, the better to examine her wan face.

'You look washed-out.' His tone was dry, caustic.
'Didn't you sleep well?'

She ignored the question, not even deigning to
thank him when he drew up a chair to the table,
settled her into it, then poured out a cup of steam-
ing coffee. With a curt nod she accepted the rolls,
butter and fruit he pushed towards her, hating the
virile, healthy look of him; black hair still damp
from his morning swim; strong neck rising from the
collar of a casual shirt dark as a falcon's wing;
bronzed forearms with their matting of fine black
hairs, the rise and fall of a strong chest as, breath-
ing easily, he relaxed in his chair to resume reading.

She ate like a ravenous young animal, devouring
roll after crusty roll, spread generously with creamy
butter, mopping up melon juice with a napkin when
it ran down her chin, gulping down fragrant coffee
that was sweet nectar to her parched throat. She was
sidling from her chair, confident that his attention
was occupied, when he abandoned his newspaper to
enquire:

'Where are you going?'

'Er . . . nowhere in particular. For a walk, perhaps.'

'Don't you think,' he continued mildly, 'that this nonsense has gone on long enough? As I have no wish to become the object of speculative tongues, we must wait until a decent interval has elapsed before returning to Malta. That being so, I suggest you allow me to show you what the island has to offer. Any company, however distasteful,' his voice developed a grate, 'must be preferable to days of self-enforced solitude.'

'I . . . can't trust you.' She licked lips that were suddenly dry.

'Can't trust me to do what?' The lift of his eyebrow was wicked.

'Can't trust you *not* to——'

'Of course you can't,' he agreed, eyeing her lazily, 'and I can give no guarantees—not when you appear before me dainty as a freshly-sprung buttercup. Come,' he rose and held out a coaxing hand, 'you will enjoy a tour of the island.'

The following days would have been idyllic in less dynamic company. Tara spent fascinating hours watching elderly ladies weaving gossamer lace seated comfortably in the doorways of their own houses, their thick fingers with work-knobbled joints moving confidently amongst dozens of hanging bobbins. She was introduced to and welcomed by the Gozitans of mixed Norman, Spanish and Italian blood, dark stalwart men, small, glossy-haired women, all hard-working, deeply religious people, jovial and keenly hospitable.

'The manufacturing industry is on a very small scale here,' Falcon told her, 'owing to the limited domestic market and lack of resources.'

There were, however, various small light industries, and he stood by amused while she became engrossed in the progress of a piece of wood being sawn, planed, carved and polished until it became a fine item of furniture. She marvelled at the intricacies of rope-making, questioned closely the methods used to produce cheese, tomato paste and wine.

'It's such a relief,' she confided, 'to visit a foreign country and yet to understand and be understood. Although I've noticed that among themselves the older people speak in a strange tongue.'

'Maltese,' he informed her, 'our own language which is akin to Arabic but which has great Italian and English influences in its vocabulary. Nowadays, all children are taught both languages and a major part of the older generation can also understand and speak English.'

They had just left the cheese processing plant and were driving along a winding coast road with, showing around every curve and bend, glimpses of sandy beaches lapped by clear blue sea. When the road began descending and the nose of the car dipped downwards towards an empty stretch of beach Tara became wary. During the past days, even though Falcon had made no promises, he had behaved perfectly. Her skin had often burned beneath meaningful looks, he had caused colour to rise in her cheeks with teasing remarks, her pulses to react violently at an accidental touch, but all the time there had been people around to insulate her from his disturbing presence. Down on the beach there was no one.

'Shouldn't we be making back to the villa?' she asked, a nerve fluttering in her throat. 'Maria will be wondering what's become of us.'

'I thought she and Paul deserved a day off,' he replied, straight-faced. 'They have gone to visit relatives—but don't worry, little glutton,' he reverted to the teasing tone that set her immediately on guard, 'you won't be allowed to starve. There is a picnic hamper in the boot, also swimsuits and towels in case we should decide to swim. I could comfortably manage without—indeed, I prefer to swim nude—but such debauchery, I suspect, would offend your Celtic prudery to the limit so, reluctantly, I shall observe the rules of propriety.'

She wanted to play safe by remaining silent, but this was the second time he had implied a naïveté she felt was totally unjustified.

'I am not, as you seem to think, a backward Irish colleen, I was not brought up in a convent, nor have I spent best part of my life in seclusion fingering rosary beads,' she told him coldly, 'neither do I recoil in horror at the very mention of the Pill.'

He slanted her a look before negotiating the car around a bend. 'So you are a product of the permissive age? A free-thinking, wild-living, liberated lady.'

He was mocking her. With difficulty, she retained her cool. 'Not that either. But I do resent

men such as yourself who insist upon regarding
women either as sex symbols or domesticated zom-
bies. Women are complex individuals with complex
problems, real people, not plastic dolls without any
thought in their heads other than dressing up to
attract the attentions of men.'

In spite of the intensity of her argument he refused to take her seriously. Drawing the car to a
halt, he switched off the engine, slid his arm across
the back of her seat, and leant closer to confide, 'It
surprises me that you should regard the talent your
sex possesses for beguiling men with such contempt
—especially when you yourself are such an exponent
of the art.'

They proceeded the rest of the way on foot, clam-
bering down a path just wide enough to accommodate one person at a time, so obstructed by a
tangle of shoulder-high vegetation it had obviously
not been used for a very long time. Falcon led the
way, holding aside branches that would have whip-
ped across her face, stamping down nettles which
might have lacerated feet left bare by thonged
sandals. Her misgivings grew when finally she stepped on to the beach and looked around at a cove
curved like outflung arms ready to embrace. Behind,
dense thicket screened them from the sight of anyone who might be passing on the road above, and
in front, a solitary stretch of sea, unmarked by sail
or buoy, or any other hint of mankind. The beach
was devoid of footsteps, a narrow stretch of sand
that would not have been out of place on a deserted
atoll.

Tara felt like a castaway when, as a shiver feathered her skin, she decided, 'I don't feel like swimming today. If you don't mind I'll just sit here and sunbathe.'

'Coward!' His deep-throated chuckle sounded in her ears like a complacent growl. To avoid having to meet his eyes she opened the picnic basket, spread the gay chequered cloth Maria had provided flat upon the sand and began setting out the contents —cold roast duck with a delicate hint of orange flavouring retained from the sauce in which it had been basted; patties baked fresh that morning, packed with minced veal, ham and chopped egg; breadsticks, long and crisp, which Maria knew were her favourites; huge tomatoes full of sun-sweet flavour; ripe strawberries and a carton of thick yellow cream. Then finally two bottles of wine, sweet for herself, dry for Falcon.

He insisted upon swimming before they ate. 'Just a swift, cooling dip!' he shouted from behind a rock while he changed. 'After which I shall be anxious to savour to the full all that the gods have provided!'

When he emerged, wearing briefs black as his dancing eyes, she was made aware that she was the item most likely to tempt his appetite. Hastily she turned away, but was not quick enough to hide from him the sight of green eyes deepening with panic, cheeks aflame with embarrassed colour, and a full bottom lip that reacted with a sensuous tremor to a weakness that shot through her body—a curious phenomenon that was new and yet familiar, exquisite in the way that pain can be exquisite ...

His laughter was still ringing in her ears when he reached the water's edge and dived in. She toyed with the idea of making a dash for the car but knew that, though seemingly engrossed in the enjoyment of his swim, his watchful eyes were upon her. She had no illusions as to why he had brought her here, his every look, every word, every touch, told of an urgent need. He had given her time, had been considerate and thoughtful, but now his days of abstinence were beginning to pall—she was his wife, and he wanted her!

She felt deeply afraid, not so much of him as of herself. If there was to be a fight she must win it by reminding herself that she hated him, must think of Aithne. *Keep thinking of Aithne!*

But when he raced out of the sea and flung himself down, still dripping wet, beside her, he seemed hungry only for food, and as he proceeded to satisfy his appetite she became able gradually to swallow the food that had seemed permanently lodged in her throat. She was even able to exchange a smile when, looking up, she saw his amusement at her childish enjoyment of crunching on a breadstick.

He was close, but harmlessly so, with a portion of duck in one hand and a bottle of wine in the other. It was while she was staring dreamily out to sea that his hand pushed back the hem of her skirt and he bent to place a kiss just above her knee. 'Tara!' he groaned, then pushed her flat against the sand. His head blotted out the sun, reason became confounded by lips tasting of wine, drugged wine that sapped her will, intoxicating wine she wanted to drain to the very dregs.

Remember Aithne!

The warning echoed faintly in her mind, then strengthened until the boom filled her ears. Her warm lips grew cold, her body stiffened, chilling to ice in his arms. He tried with all the urgency within him to get her to respond, tenderly, then more desperately as frustration took its toll. The grip of his hands was torture, his voice savage, as unbearably aggravated, he threatened, 'I will take you as a slave girl, if I must!'

This time there were no magical moments, no waves of mutual passion carrying them to sublime heights, just a nightmare created by a man driven to vent his anger and frustration upon the bride whose impassive acceptance made him ashamed.

Bitterness was etched into his features when finally he flung away. 'Purgatory is woman! You may be a novice to love, Tara, but you certainly know how to punish!'

Left suddenly alone, she sank back on to the sand and closed her eyes tightly to force back tears. Punishment meant pain. She had become a close associate of pain—a pain so consuming it seemed always to have been with her and, what was most intolerable, so deeply embedded she could not foresee that it would ever fade.

CHAPTER FIVE

Aithne and O'Toole had arrived in Malta. Paul had taken the telephone message then passed it on to Falcon, who in turn shocked Tara with the news the following morning.

'It seems that your father and sister arrived in the capital last night. They have booked in an hotel for the time being but, naturally, they must not be allowed to remain there. Their arrival has provided us with the excuse we need to curtail our ...' he paused, 'honeymoon. We can return now to Valetta where I have a town house, and they can join us there.'

Slowly Tara continued buttering a roll she had no intention of eating. He sounded relieved at the prospect of leaving. He had greeted her arrival at the breakfast table in a manner very different from his usual teasing banter, his face stern, his voice clipped, and on several occasions she had suspected that he had deliberately avoiding looking her way. She had no need to guess why. Falzon pride was rampant. Yesterday he had reached the very edge of endurance, had reached out for a wife he knew could be loving and giving in a shy yet passionate way that delighted him, only to find her reacting like a nun. To punish such aggravation he had taken her in the manner of a sheikh with a slave girl, but she had known from his expression and from the bitterness in his voice that victory had been hers—not his. Probably for the first time in his life the proud Baron had experienced debasement. His present attitude was evidence that he had not forgiven her for inflicting upon his conscience a burden so onerous it had stamped deep creases of concern upon his brow.

'If you will excuse me,' he rose to his feet and towered, politely aloof, 'I'll leave you to finish breakfast while I make arrangements for our departure.'

Tara stared at his retreating back, unaware that the roll she had been holding had been reduced to a pile of shredded crumbs. Even in childhood, whenever she had been made to feel guilty, her reaction had invariably been one of indignant scorn. She had not outgrown the habit. 'How typical of the man!' she fumed, fiercely stemming the tremor in her voice. 'He is the culprit, I the victim, yet he has the nerve to expect *me* to shoulder the blame! A beggar has no right to pride! He married me for money—from now on that's all he's likely to get.'

It was late afternoon when Falcon manoeuvred the speedboat between gaily painted *dghajsa*, taxi boats ferrying passengers towards land from a boat that had just dropped anchor in the Grand Harbour. A car was waiting on the quayside, its doors unlocked, keys left in the ignition, so once he had assured himself that Tara was comfortable he set off without a word, accelerating hard in order to propel the car up one of the many narrow streets, so steep they seemed almost perpendicular when viewed from the low-lying harbour. As they drove, she was reminded of Byron's farewell to the island, penned with distaste because of an unhappy love affair. 'Adieu, ye cursed streets of stairs—how surely he who mounts you swears!'

As Falcon negotiated streets of palaces, magnificent churches and crammed-in shops so narrow their wares spilled outside on to the pavements, she filled in her time trying to guess which of the many houses would be his. But when he swung the car through an archway and into a paved courtyard she was not prepared for the sight of yet another palazzo with the coat of arms of the Falzon family chipped into the stone above a huge open doorway.

At the foot of a flight of narrow steps stood a small, plump figure, jigging excitedly from one foot to the other. Falcon winced when, for the first time in days, his wife's face radiated joy as she wound down the car window to call out:

'Bridget, darling Bridget, I'm so pleased to see you!'

She tumbled from the car into waiting arms and was squeezed in a motherly hug and treated to the usual gentle scolding. 'Are those tears you're shedding, alannah?' She cast a fierce look in Falcon's direction. 'If so, they'd better be tears of happiness or someone will have to answer to Bridget Mc-Bride!'

Making a massive effort, Tara drew back to display a brilliant smile. 'It's just that I'm being over-emotional at the thought of seeing my family. Have you spoken to O'Toole? And what about Aithne, is she well?'

She noticed little of the interior of what proved to be a miniature palace, its ancient rooms converted to meet the demands of modern-day living. Sparing the main hall—comfortably luxurious yet managing with the aid of portraits, porcelain, ancient woodwork and ceramics to retain an air of dignified nobility—no more than a cursory glance, she followed Bridget up a flight of stairs, along a thickly carpeted passage, then through a doorway leading into a room that was a silent, cool contrast to the noise, heat and bustle of outdoors.

'This is your sitting-room,' Bridget informed her, seemingly quite at home. 'The door on the right leads into the main bedroom, the one on the left leads to the bathroom and beyond that is another smaller room which is also part of the suite—a dressing room, I think,' she frowned, 'containing a bed which I didn't bother to have made up, seeing no one will be using it.'

As she reached out to open shutters spanning the windows Tara pleaded, 'Leave them as they are, if you don't mind, Bridget. I prefer the room to be left dim. I ... I have a slight headache.'

Conscious of Bridget's assessing eye, she sank down on to a settee covered in green sprigged linen and with as much composure as she could muster, considering the nuptial nature of her surroundings, she patted the space next to her.

'Come, sit down and tell me everything you know about Aithne and O'Toole. What brought them to

Malta? And what was their reaction when they learned of my marriage?'

Nothing loath, Bridget sat down and with her hands folded in her lap prepared to enjoy a good long gossip. 'It was news of your marriage that brought them here. Seemingly it had been reported in all the daily papers—just think of it, child, your picture landing on the breakfast tables of people in countries all over the world! But then again,' she conceded, 'it might be that it's the Baron they find so newsworthy. O'Toole, as you can imagine, was thunderstruck.'

'And Aithne, how did she take it?'

'I don't know,' Bridget disappointed her, 'I haven't seen her yet, but the Baron has invited them both to dinner this evening, so you'll be able to find out for yourself. Your father——'

She broke off, showing annoying subservience by jumping to her feet to bob a curtsey when Falcon stepped into the room. He waited, smiling charmingly as she made a hurried exit, then closed the door behind her and advanced to take a seat directly opposite the couch where Tara was sitting.

'Is everything to your liking?' he enquired smoothly.

Made angry by her own nervousness, she replied with heat, 'No, it is not! I see no reason why we should be sharing a room.'

'A suite of rooms,' he corrected.

'Split hairs if you must,' she countered, 'but the fact remains that I shall feel safer in a room of my own.'

Raised eyebrows denigrated her unfortunate choice of phrase, yet his tone sounded unruffled as he went on to explain, 'As we agreed, I have invited your father and sister to stay with us for the duration of their visit to Malta. Unfortunately, although the palazzo may appear large a lot of the rooms that were unsuitable for conversion have been allowed to fall into disuse. Consequently, once your family arrives, all the available rooms will be occupied, which means, I'm afraid, that you will have to endure my close proximity. There is a further reason, of course, one which should not require explanation.'

'And that is?' Her chin jutted defiance.

'That I do not wish your family to guess at the rather delicate state of our relationship. All newlyweds have disagreements, this is perfectly natural, and I presume your father is experienced enough in the ways of the world to view such a situation with tolerance, if ever he were to become aware of its existence. However, I dislike having my affairs discussed, so I must insist upon your giving me your word that you will do and say nothing that might give rise to a suspicion that all is not well between us.'

'Insist away!' Pride inherited from a long line of chieftains was evident in her stance as she jumped to her feet, defiant of what she considered to be a threat. 'You will receive no such promise from me, just as soon as I'm able I intend asking my father's advice about obtaining a divorce. He's an expert in such matters,' she boasted, 'having gone through the process three times himself.'

'Which helps to explain,' he said icily, 'why his daughter has so little respect for the sanctity of marriage!'

'Sanctity of marriage!' she snapped, her rage now as fiery as her hair. 'How dare you insult my intelligence by implying that the motive that prompted your proposal was anything other than mercenary! Did you *really* expect me to believe that you'd fallen deeply and sincerely in love with me only weeks after seducing my sister?'

Impatience impelled him to his feet. Behind him, sun slanted through slatted shutters, casting his dark, imperious shadow across her face. 'I have never *had* your sister, nor do I want your money,' he spelled out with a bluntness she found shocking. As she stared, disconcerted, his anger disappeared so quickly she was caught unawares. Without having seemed to have moved he appeared close enough to pull her into an embrace left deliberately light, giving her the option either or remaining or jerking away.

She was too nonplussed to move even when, placing his lips lightly against her temple, he urged, 'Think back to the first night of our marriage, Tara, remember, as I so often do, the mutual bliss, the shared passion that left us both shaken, full of unbelievable joy. I adored my shy, wanton, tempestuous, subdued, fearful yet courageous bride—and you did not hate me, not all of the time. Admit it, Tara, be honest with me—and with yourself ...' His plea was breathed against her ear. She swayed towards him, caught once again in the strands of a magical web that cast a veil over misgivings and made oblivious of pride, anger—even Aithne.

Aithne! Just in time she jerked back to sanity. Enraged by her own weakness, she dared to storm, 'I'm grateful for the sample of technique you employ in order to exploit gullible women. Unfortunately, it was completely wasted on me, but don't despair, Baron, there are plenty of women who aren't so particular as I! Why don't you cut your losses and give me my freedom before,' she speared the ultimate insult, 'you are deprived of your only asset—virility has been known to wane; tarry too long and you might discover that desire is beginning to outlive performance!'

Colour rose under his tan—proof that he was not entirely brute—then drained away, leaving his features set into a mask of disdain. Tara was trembling in her shoes, but Falcon was not allowed to guess this as he gave vent to his disgust.

'For the first time, I find myself wishing that you were a man.'

'So that you might hit me?' Her jeer tailed into a gulp.

'So that I might gain satisfaction from physical retribution, yes,' he agreed coldly. 'But then,' his eyes narrowed to slits, 'I need hardly remind you that there is another method of physical punishment that leaves no scars upon the body, yet sears the soul. Tread warily, Tara, think twice in future before uttering an impulsive word or carrying out an impulsive action, otherwise I shall have to teach you

the wisdom of discretion—a wisdom that can only
be gained through suffering.'

Tara had just finished dressing for dinner when,
after a tap upon the door, Aithne walked into the
room dressed in an evening gown of pale blue, her
blonde hair, cat-sleek, hanging down past her
shoulders. She looked like a pretty doll, Tara
thought, but a doll whose pretty face was marred
by a petulant scowl.

'Aithne!' Tara stepped eagerly to greet her, only
to hesitate, puzzled, when Aithne side-stepped to
avoid her.

'So you've managed to do it again!' Aithne
charged, her voice harsh and accusing.

'Done it again?' Tara echoed stupidly. 'I don't
understand.'

'Of course you don't, dear sister!' Aithne sneered.
'But only because it suits your purpose not to! How
else could you bribe your conscience, if not by
refusing to admit even to yourself that you deliberately set out to ensnare every man who takes my
fancy?'

Tara stared, bewilderment chasing across her
features.

'And you can spare me the mealy-mouthed
denials,' Aithne stamped her foot, obviously working herself up, as was her wont whenever she was
thwarted, into a childish tantrum. 'For years I've
stood your hypocritical teasing about my inability to
settle with one man, knowing full well that I've
never been given a choice because you've com-
mandeered every man I've been foolish enough to

introduce into the family circle. Half an hour in your company was enough to make them lose interest in me, which was exactly what you intended. Oh, you didn't want them for yourself,' she tossed her head, 'all you wanted was to exercise your power, to show how easily it could be done, caring nothing about my happiness nor of the feelings of the men who, once they were hooked, received the cold shoulder!'

'Aithne!' Tara could not believe that it was her young sister mouthing such wild accusations, the girl she had mothered, protected from infancy, the sister she had first glimpsed as a minute bundle of helplessness lying in a cot which she herself had barely been able to reach. 'It isn't true, you *must* know it isn't true! I've never consciously harmed you in any way!'

With a most unladylike snort, Aithne challenged, 'Then why are you here? What possible motive could you have had for coming to Malta, an island the existence of which had barely registered on your consciousness until I told you about Falcon and how much he meant to me?'

'I admit it must seem strange.' Tara was trembling so much she could hardly stand, she needed to sit down, needed time to digest the fact that the sister she loved seemed almost to hate her. 'But I can explain. Look, let's go into the sitting-room,' she glanced down at her watch, 'we've just fifteen minutes before we'll be expected downstairs for dinner.'

With a look of dislike Tara found hard to weather

Aithne flounced towards the doorway of the adjoining room, her rigid frame spelling out the fact that she was in no mood to listen to, much less believe any explanation that might be forthcoming. But when they were both seated, something about Tara's white, unhappy face stirred her curiosity; she did not have the look of a radiantly happy bride; her green eyes, usually so clear and sparkling with self-confidence seemed haunted, her once unshakeable composure had given way to a tense nervousness. Yet she still managed to look astonishingly beautiful, Aithne reluctantly admitted, envying her her swan-like grace of movement, startling eyes fringed with thick, sooty lashes, and a glorious mane of hair inherited from their maternal grandmother. 'It's not surprising that you're spoiled,' she charged bitterly. 'All your life you've had everything you've ever wanted—even Grandmother Rooney was so enchanted by the fact that you'd been fashioned in her image that she left you everything she owned—sparing not so much as a brass tack for me!'

'That was most unfair of her,' Tara gently agreed, 'but I've always intended sharing my inheritance with you. In a month's time, when the money is due to come to me, you'll receive half. After all, there's more than enough for two.'

Slightly mollified, Aithne acknowledged the promise with a brief nod, encouraging Tara to continue with her explanation. 'I came here deliberately to seek out Baron Falzon, but not for the reason you think.'

The formality with which she had mentioned

her husband's name was so surprising Aithne remained silent, wanting to hear more. 'I came to punish him for turning the head of a young, innocent child to the extent of allowing him to seduce her.' This time, after a visible start, Aithne tried to interrupt, but Tara would not be halted; her temper was high, her indignation in full flood. 'There's no need for you to feel embarrassed or ashamed; the Baron is a past master of the art of seduction—even I, who came here hating him, couldn't remain entirely immune from his spurious attraction. Luckily,' Tara allowed herself one small lie, 'I'm less gullible than most.'

Aithne jerked erect. 'Correct me if I'm wrong, but I thought you'd married the man!'

'The marriage was a mistake.'

'A mistake!' Aithne's curiosity was now raging. 'How is it possible ...?'

'My intention was to jilt him at the last moment, but I left it too late. It was the atmosphere ...' Tara faltered, 'the sound of children singing hymns; the hushed solemnity inside the cathedral, the Baron's stern expression. Oh, everything ...!' She waved a hand vaguely in the air. 'A combination of circumstances that made it impossible for me to carry out my plan, and before I realised it, the ring had been slipped on my finger and I was Baroness Falzon.'

Aithne sagged in her chair, made breathless by the enormity of her sister's daring. Not for one second did she doubt that Tara was telling the truth; she was noted for her recklessness, had been warned time after time by an anxious Bridget that no good would come of her disregard for the consequences of audacious actions. All during their childhood it had been Tara who had been the one to urge her pony to jump fences no one else dared tackle, she who had pitted her strength against dangerous currents in order to win a dare, she who had revelled in the excitement of piloting a plane and who had even—though Bridget and O'Toole had remained blissfully unaware—risked life and limb during a parachute jumping craze.

'Tara, you're a fool,' she told her without heat, 'but I doubt if you need anyone to tell you that now.' As a thought crossed her mind she leant forward to question narrowly. 'And what of Falcon, is he aware of all you have told me?'

'Of course!' There was dignity in her reply, the dignity of one who prides herself upon her honesty. She wondered at the way Aithne's tongue flicked nervously across her lips before she ventured the question:

'And what was his reaction when you accused him of seducing me?'

'Naturally he denied it, but he would, wouldn't he? He even had the gall to deny ever having met you. I replied to this piece of nonsense by telling him that I prefer to take your word before his.'

Aithne made a small choking sound. When her cheeks flooded with brilliant colour Tara moved swiftly to comfort her. Dropping to her knees by her side, she hugged her, promising faithfully, 'You shall still be revenged. As soon as possible I shall ask O'Toole's advice about getting a divorce. Knowing how poor the Baron is, I tried to bribe him with money, but to my surprise he refused to even consider the idea. It seems that divorce is still regarded as a cardinal sin here in Malta and as his pride will not allow him to become involved in unsavoury scandal he insists that the marriage must stand. However,' she rose to her feet, looking fiercely determined, 'as O'Toole has often affirmed, there's nothing that money can't buy. Grandmother Rooney's inheritance will be used to purchase my freedom from an unwanted encumbrance.' She wondered why Aithne was staring so long and curiously, but when she seemed about to speak, Tara glanced at her watch and forestalled her. 'I'm sorry, but further discussion must wait—we're already ten minutes late for dinner. Don't worry too much about this meeting with Falcon,' she gave Aithne's arm an encouraging squeeze as they left the room to make their way downstairs, 'it's bound to be embarrassing, but remember I'll be right beside you, backing you all the way.'

CHAPTER SIX

A QUIET family dinner had been planned, so only Falcon and O'Toole were present when Tara and Aithne entered the room. They were both drinking wine, Falcon's glass still almost full and O'Toole's nearly empty. Noting her father's flushed countenance, Tara wondered if it were his second or possibly even his third pre-dinner drink. Knowing his penchant for the good things of life she guessed that it was one of several. Her frown disappeared, however, when, at the sight of her, he opened his arms wide and she ran into them, to be chided, kissed and almost squeezed to death.

'Sly little devil!' He demonstrated fond disapproval by raising his huge palm and smacking it hard against her bottom. 'How dare you run off and get married without informing your family!'

Indignantly, she pushed him away. The hard thwack had resounded around the room and her flesh was smarting beneath the fine, clinging material of her dress. As her father bellowed with laughter she looked up and was further enraged by the quirk of amusement on Falcon's lips. Her heart sank when her father continued to bellow:

'Don't fret about it, darling girl—having introduced myself to my new son-in-law I'm now prepared to forgive you. You've made an admirable choice.'

She needed no further confirmation of the suspicion that he had already over-imbibed. The evening ahead promised to be a difficult one—O'Toole sober could be incorrigible; when tipsy he was invariably an embarrassment.

Chained by conversation to his side, she could do no more than watch covertly as Falcon approached Aithne to offer her a drink.

'Sherry?' he suggested, his unfathomable look scanning Aithne's rather frightened face.

'That will do nicely,' she gulped, attempting bravado. Making no move to fetch the drink, he remained staring down at her, his eyes pinpointing every nervous tremor, each agitated blink of her eyelids. 'I believe,' he continued without a smile, 'that we have met before—that we have shared an intimate relationship?'

It was as well Tara could not hear Aithne's reply. With blue eyes limpid, she gazed up into his eyes and pleaded, 'Please, don't blame me. My sister has an aptitude for jumping to wrong conclusions. I must admit,' coyly, her lashes swept downwards, 'to the small vanity of implying that during my stay in Malta we became good friends, whereas we were in fact no more than acquaintances.'

'I must be ungallant and admit that the acquaintanceship was, on my part, so casual it failed even to register.'

The dryness of his tone brought a fresh flood of colour to her cheeks, yet boldly she insisted, 'But we bumped into each other at lots of different

parties! We seemed always to be running with the
same crowd—don't you remember dancing with
me at the de Marcos' anniversary celebration?'

'No.'

The bald denial shook her, yet his attraction was
such that she refused to be deflated. During the
duration of her holiday she had hovered on the
brink of his social scene, turning up at every function she knew he was to attend, waiting desperately
to be noticed, but being left dejected each evening
by her seeming inability to register upon his conscience. But here, in his house, she could not possibly be overlooked. The advantages seemed to be
all on her side—Tara, once her mind was made up,
was immovable; Falcon was reputed to possess
more than his share of healthy virile ability. The
combination of a wife frigid with dislike and a
husband frustrated by enforced celibacy was an
explosive one, and when the fuse was lit she wanted
to be around to pick up the pieces.

To Tara's observant eye, they seemed to be enjoying a casual conversation as Falcon led Aithne
across to the drinks table, but she was unable to
see his eyes glittering cold as the diamonds in his
cuffs when, handing Aithne her sherry, he enquired:

'And is it your intention to allow Tara to continue thinking the worst?'

Her worried blue eyes traced his features, the
grimness of a mouth showing distaste at being
forced to discuss his most intimate affairs with an
outsider; the knotting of a muscle in his jaw bely-

ing the suavity of his manner.

'Believe me, Falcon,' she assured him in her best imitation of a heartbroken whisper, 'I've tried to explain, but Tara either can't or won't accept that there was a misunderstanding.' She sighed deeply. 'It's almost as if she doesn't want to believe me, but that's a silly assumption ... isn't it?' When a tightening of his jawline was her only answer, she continued to press her advantage. 'Falcon, I love my sister dearly and I want to do everything I can to help you both, which is why I dare to suggest ...' Delicately she paused.

'Please do go on,' he requested coldly.

'Well,' she shrugged, 'it's just that, knowing Tara as I do, I believe her incapable of appreciating anything, *or anyone*, she hasn't striven to obtain. She's quite determined to divorce you—'

His head snapped up. 'She told you *that*?'

Aithne's pulses leapt. The Baron's pride was on the rack, his knuckles showing white around the stem of his glass.

'Please don't be angry with her—we've always made a habit of confiding in each other, which is why I dare to suggest that if you want to keep your wife you'll need to make her suspect that you no longer want her.'

'Arouse her jealousy, you mean?' His tone was uncomfortably dry. 'But that would mean my having to rely upon the co-operation of another woman, and how can I be sure that whomsoever I might choose would not read too much into my attentions?'

Aithne trod as carefully as she would over thorns. 'By relying upon someone you know is aware of all the facts and is anxious to atone for any unhappiness she may unwittingly have caused.'

He was not fooled, yet she sensed that something about her suggestion appealed to him. 'Are you a lamb offering yourself as sacrifice?'

Hiding a glint of triumph beneath lowered lashes, she whispered the reply, 'I'm Tara's sister, willing to endure whatever is necessary to achieve her happiness.'

Dinner was a delicious gastronomical experience, superbly cooked, expertly served, and with a different choice of wine to accompany each course. Much to Tara's embarrassment, her father drank two glasses of wine to everyone else's one. Praising Falcon's expertise in mating dry Madeira with consommé; a sharper fine sherry with smoked eels, and with sweetbreads—a grand dish calling for a grand wine—a well-matured Burgundy that complemented perfectly the sauce in which the dish had been cooked. The dessert of wild strawberries soaked in red Bordeaux did not satisfy him; he insisted upon having more of the wine poured into his glass.

'I say, Falcon!' He sat back, more than a little glassy-eyed. 'I need have no qualms about my daughter's future if you gave to your partnership as much thought as you've given to the mating of food and wine. That was no mere meal, but a superb blending of taste and quality—the exact ingredients needed to achieve a perfect marriage.'

Falcon acknowledged the compliment with a shrug. 'I am impatient of rules and regulations governing which wine goes with which food, but there is a vast supply of accumulated experience that only a fool would ignore. I am guided mostly by that which I, personally, have found to be good. I am pleased that you approve my choice.'

'It would be difficult not to approve,' O'Toole replied with a sly grin. 'How can I fault your taste when you've just deprived me of the best of what I own? Though I say so myself,' he grinned fatuously at Tara, 'my daughter could have taken her pick of Irish manhood. But no, not just Irishmen,' he corrected himself, 'for everywhere she has gone men have been bowled over by her beauty, I can't tell you the number of drinks that have been pressed upon me, how many favours have been extended simply as a ploy to effect an introduction. Not that it did any of them any good,' he chuckled. 'She's a spirited mare, my Tara, who needs a firm hand on the reins. She never could abide a man who allowed her too much of her own way.'

Behind her mask of cool unconcern Tara felt aghast. Her father was being his usual outrageous self; in the past she had shrugged off his inclination towards intemperance, had laughed at his jokes, had even been inclined to admire his arrogance, but tonight in the company of the fastidiously polite, perfectly-mannered Baron she began seeing her father in a different light. Had he always been so coarse in manner, so loud of voice. His frame was massive, huge in every respect, but she had never

previously noticed heavy jowls that hinted at glut-
tony and a mouth that slobbered slightly when he
ate and drank. She sensed dislike hidden behind
Falcon's over-polite conversation, heard hauteur
so slight it was audible only to her ears, contained
in the voice uttering suave replies.

'Tara is the very spit of old Mother Rooney,
d'you know—my late mother-in-law.' O'Toole
reached out to help himself to a chunk of cheese.
'The very devil of a woman, she was. *My God*,' he
digressed, 'this cheese has one hell of a bite!'

'Roquefort,' Falcon supplied, his jaw tight. 'A
cheese so strongly flavoured no accompanying wine
would stand a chance of being tasted.'

O'Toole's regret was obvious. Swallowing his
disappointment with the last of the cheese, he continued to enlarge upon the subject of his late,
obviously unlamented mother-in-law. 'Yes, she was
a spalpeen, that she was! A famous horsewoman in
her day who, legend has it, rode through the countryside astride a half-wild stallion looking, with her
hair streaming out behind her, like some demented
red-haired witch. But she met her match in Rooney,
I can tell you,' he rumbled a laugh, patting his
bulging stomach. 'In time, Rooney tamed her tantrums, but she gave him a hard mission. I've been
told by one who knows it to be the truth,' he leant
across the table to confide, 'that on the first night of
their marriage Rooney had to beat her before she
would share his bed!'

For one startled second Tara's eyes flashed upwards and clashed with a dark stare lightened by a

glint of amusement. Immediately she looked away, feeling relieved that neither Aithne nor O'Toole seemed aware of the mute exchange that was to blame for the high rise of colour in her cheeks.

Unable to bear another minute of her father's reminiscences, she rose to her feet and suggested:

'Shall we take coffee in the sitting-room?'

'You two girls go ahead,' her father waved an expansive hand, 'this is the first real chance I've had to talk to your husband. We'll join you later.'

She knew better than to argue with him in his present mood, so she and Aithne had no choice but to retire into the adjoining room where, once the door had closed behind them, she began pacing the floor in a fever of impatience.

'Do sit down,' Aithne ordered crossly, 'you're making me feel quite nervous.'

'I must talk to Father.' Tara's brow creased. 'Besides, I don't want him getting too friendly with the Baron, there's really no *point*!' She sat down opposite Aithne. 'By the way, how did your confrontation go? Did he try to continue with his bluff of pretending that you're unknown to him?'

'Quite the reverse,' Aithne surprised her. 'As a matter of fact we discussed the last time we met at the de Marcos' anniversary party, when we danced together all evening.'

'Oh ...' For some unknown reason Tara could get no further words past her tight throat. She had felt certain Falcon would have continued to insist upon his innocence, would, at the first opportunity, have accused Aithne of lying and might even have continued the pretence far enough to refuse to have her under his roof. All of these things she had been prepared for, but his easy approach, their casual, friendly exchange of conversation, had been the very last thing she had expected.

'How can you bear to even speak to him!' she choked.

'I love him,' Aithne told her calmly. 'I don't care that he is your husband, I knew him long before you did, I have the prior claim.' Her chin jutted defiantly. 'I'm pleased to know that you don't want him—because I *certainly* do!' She stood up and began sauntering around the room, looking anywhere but at her sister's horrified face. 'Are you aware of any law that decrees it's wrong of a woman to marry her divorced sister's husband?' she asked casually.

'You wouldn't!' Tara gasped.

'But yes, sister dear,' Aithne mocked, 'I most definitely would!'

Slowly Tara undressed, slipped into a dressing gown, then positioned a chair close to the window of her bedroom where she could sit looking down into the courtyard. She had asked Aithne to make her excuses to the two men; she knew Falcon would not be pleased by her absence, but she had felt incapable of remaining for one moment longer in the same room as her sister. For some reason their relationship had undergone a change; she could not pinpoint exactly how or when the change had occurred, but there was a lack of sympathy between them and a boldness in Aithne that she had found shocking.

She was puzzled by her own as well as by Aithne's reactions. Granted, she had married Falcon knowing her sister to be in love with him, but she had expected Aithne, in her usual flirtatious way, to console herself with some new admirer. Her declaration that she still loved Falcon had come as a great shock—but the shock of hearing her declare that she intended to marry Falcon once their divorce had been finalised had been much greater. She had been shaken by the news, had even, for a brief moment, felt an emotion akin to possessiveness. But that was ridiculous—the traumatic events of the past few days were having a softening influence on her brain.

She sat for a further hour, too dispirited to delve deeper into thoughts which when she tried to sort them out seemed to become more and more entangled. Then her ears alerted to the sound of footsteps progressing along the passageway outside, heavy, stumbling footsteps that could only belong to O'Toole!

She ran across to the door and yanked it open just in time to see him stepping over the threshold of his bedroom. She ran the length of the passageway, tapped on the door, then without waiting for permission stepped inside the room. Her father was standing next to his bed, swaying slightly, but his head jerked up when she entered.

'Well, hello, my clever child!' he burbled. 'Have you come to help your old father into bed?'

'I have not,' she crisped. 'I've come to have a

talk, a long, serious talk.'

'I'm in no mood for such rubbish! Here, darlin', help me off with my shoes, my feet are killing me.'

Biting back her vexation, Tara slid the shoes from his feet, helped him into a dressing gown, then, when he was comfortably seated, astonished him sober by demanding:

'Father, I want to know what I must do to get a divorce.' As he stared, deplete of words, she rushed on, 'In a few weeks' time I'm due my inheritance, whatever the cost, I must have a divorce. *I must ...!*'

Giving a great heave, O'Toole stood up to bluster, 'You don't know what you're saying, child! Your marriage is just over a week old, sometimes it can take years for a man and a woman to settle down together—give it a working chance, for heaven's sake!'

'No!' Tara's face took on the mutinous expression he dreaded. 'I want a divorce and I want it as soon as is humanly possible.'

'Why?' he bellowed. 'Does your husband beat you? Having a bride of just over a week he's hardly likely to be casting his eyes over other women, so why, girl, you must have a reason?'

'We ... we're incompatible!' she suggested wildly. 'Also he's a beast and I hate him—*hate him!*'

O'Toole looked her over thoughtfully before maddening her with the observation, 'That's a mighty good sign. This is the first time I've seen your emotions aroused to fever pitch by any man.

Are you sure it's hatred you feel for him and not love? So far as my eye can judge you're too over-wrought to know the difference.'

'Father!' She drew herself up to ask with dignity, 'Are you going to help me or not? If your answer is to be no then I can easily find out all I need to know from other sources. Money, I'm happy to say, is of no consequence; even after sharing with Aithne there'll be more than enough left for my needs.'

To her surprise he suddenly crumpled and slumped back into his chair to sit with head bowed, chin sunk deep into his chest. For a moment she suspected he had fallen into a drunken sleep and was just about to leave when he called her back, his voice sober, unutterably weary. 'Don't go, Tara, there's something I must tell you.'

She waited, stock-still, her back turned towards him. Something about his tone had sent an ominous prickling up her spine. 'Yes, Father, I'm waiting ... ?'

'I meant to tell you sooner,' he began heavily, 'but I kept putting it off ...' His voice trailed into nothingness.

'And now you've decided that whatever it is you have to tell me can't be put off any longer?' She turned in time to catch his nod, then stepped towards him to accuse hardly, 'Knowing your incurable optimism, your habit of pushing unpleasant matters to one side in the hope that they'll some-how disappear, I must surmise that some day of judgment is almost upon you. Which day of judgment, Father?'

'The day you're supposed to receive your inheritance,' he admitted, unable to meet her eyes. 'Believe me, child, at the time, I thought that what I did was for the best, my motive was to increase your money instead of ...'

'Instead of ...?' she prompted, her voice a mere thread of sound.

'It's gone, Tara, all gone,' he admitted heavily. 'As you know, the estate was left in my hands, the money to be administered at my discretion, for your benefit, to see to your comforts until you were of an age to inherit. And that is exactly what I did,' he assured her, seeming genuinely to believe his own words. 'Not a penny of your money did I touch until last year when I was given some confidential information that was supposed to enable me to make a killing on the Stock Exchange. I lost all that I'd invested, then began gambling to try to get back what I'd lost, but my winning streak evaded me until finally I became snowed under with debts— alimony payments, bills for this, bills for that ...' With a hint of temper he spun his head to accuse, 'And you two girls didn't help! D'you know, there was a time when I had to settle bills for dresses costing over two hundred pounds *each*! You're extravagant minxes, the pair of you!'

'We were brought up to be extravagant,' Tara choked. 'You *encouraged* us!'

They remained glaring at each other until O'Toole dropped his eyes. 'Anyway,' he sighed, 'it was then that I began to borrow from your inheritance, salving my conscience by telling myself that the money was being used for your own good. Perhaps I should have tried to economise, but I was so convinced that luck was just around the corner.'

'Father!' The significance of what he had been saying was only just beginning to sink in. 'Exactly how much money is left?'

'None, I'm afraid. We're both of us broke, flat stony broke! However,' he stared at her, pathetically eager, 'our luck *has* changed—or rather it *can* be changed, with the help of your husband.'

Her stare was blankly incomprehending. 'Falcon?' she asked dully. 'Don't be silly!'

'Why shouldn't he help!' O'Toole roared, enraged by what he considered to be deliberate obtuseness. 'The bloody man's a multi-millionaire!'

CHAPTER SEVEN

SOMEHOW Tara stumbled back to her bedroom and groped her way towards the chair by the window. She felt stunned, a blow from a bludgeon could have had no greater impact than her father's words. And yet, she reflected, trembling into her seat, the signs had all been there to read had she not been so blinded by her own predetermined opinion of Falcon's character. She had labelled him playboy, gigolo, even one who danced attendance upon wealthy women in order to achieve financial gain. She winced. Not even the wealthiest of women could have provided him with sufficient money to pay the upkeep of a ruinously expensive palazzo, an elegant town house and a villa in Gozo designed and built for the use of a man of opulent tastes and the wealth with which to indulge them. The powerful sports car, the sleek speedboat, might both have been rented to impress—she knew now that they were not.

How amused he must have been by her offer to buy him off! She jumped up, agitated beyond belief, struggling to adjust to this startling new image that her father had so confidently presented. Phrases he had used harassed her mind: 'Have you no eyes in your head, girl?' he had roared. 'Five minutes after stepping on to Maltese soil I was confronted by evidence of your husband's wealth. On the wharves were buildings with nameplates bearing in letters a foot high, Falzon Shipping Company; Falzon Boatbuilding and Repair Yards, and along the road-sides directions leading to the House of Falzon, ex-porters of fine glass, the Falzon Winery, the Falzon Estate Agency! From newspapers I discovered him to be a director of the casino, of this insurance company, of that bank—the list is as endless as his money, so you need feel no qualms about approach-ing him to help your father with a loan.'

'I'll die first!' she had spat, before running out of the room, and she had meant every word ... Falcon had treated her like a fool, listening to her ravings with imperturbable calm while all the time laughing up his sleeve.

Her glance sharpened when down in the court-yard something moved, it was a shadow—two shadows—merging with the dark outline of the fountain positioned in the centre of the courtyard. She peered downward, suspecting prowlers, then jerked back when the moon sailed from behind cloud to expose Aithne sliding her arms around Falcon's neck while he, his head bent close, smiled down into her face.

Wild temper shot, flame-sharp, through her veins. Grandmother Rooney's money might have gone, but her legacy of pride, temper and spirit still remained. Resentment urged her to rush down-stairs to confront them both, but a quick glance out of the window told her that they were no longer there. She heard Aithne's tinkling laughter and realised they were on their way upstairs, so she waited, silently seething, until she heard a door close and the sound of movement coming from the adjoining dressing-room. All the force of her temper was behind the hand that crashed open the door leading into his room.

He had disposed of his jacket and tie and was just about to shrug bronzed shoulders out of his shirt when she erupted inside the room. For a second her confidence baulked, confronted by the sight of muscles rippling as, with the supple grace of a jungle prowler, he stalked his domain. But she was no mouse to be intimidated by superior physique. Courageously, she flew into attack.

'Swine!' she accused him stormily. 'Iniquitous, degenerate rogue! You took advantage of Aithne once before and now you dare to do so again—*right beneath my window!*'

Seeming not one whit disturbed by her appearance, he flung his shirt on to the bed, then turned his back on her furious stare, strolling across to a dressing-table to deposit the watch he had unhooked from around his wrist. 'Perhaps if I had a wife who was prepared to fulfil her obligations I would have no need of extra-marital affairs,' he drawled. 'Aithne is a lovely and very ... willing girl. But perhaps you are right!' he snapped his fingers decisively. 'I must be more discreet in future.'

'In future,' she stamped her foot, 'you will not go near my sister!'

His nostrils flared; obviously he disliked to be

ordered. 'Are you telling me that you're willing to take her place?'

'Blackmailer! You have a repertoire of dirty tricks!'

He strode the width of the narrow room to grab her by the shoulders. Shaking her vigorously, he clamped, 'And you astound me with your endless flow of invective! Take a good look at yourself, dear wife, and see what I see—a woman who deliberately and cold-bloodedly schemed her way into marriage with a man she professes to hate! A liar, who stood with me in front of an altar and promised to love, honour and obey! An impostor, with the face of an angel who screams insults like a virago. I have heard it said that Patrick, your country's patron saint, rid Ireland of its snakes—it would seem that in the process their venom was transferred to the tongues of its womenfolk!'

She jerked away, crimson with outrage. Never before had a man paid her anything but compliments, this new experience left her shaken, doubting her own integrity.

'I had a very good reason for doing what I did!' she reminded, hating him with her eyes.

'Because you listened to lies!' he grated, his body coiled and tense as if ready to spring. 'I find it hard to forgive myself for not seeing through your pretence of being in love with me when the only heat you generated was the heat of hatred. Unlike men, whose passions run naked, women can simulate affection, can endure undesired caresses with pretended enjoyment. During our so-called courtship I excused your reluctance to yield completely with the reminder of woman's disposition; when a man will, she won't! I congratulated myself upon acquiring an innocent bride,' his mirthless laughter grated in her ears, 'but was soon disillusioned. Physically, you were a virgin—spiritually and mentally you are a harlot!'

Tara held herself rigid, weathering the humiliation of a tongue-lashing she felt was quite undeserved.

'And are you so blameless?' she challenged, her chin outthrust. 'Did you not also cheat when you married me instead of my sister? Did you not also deceive by allowing me to believe that you were poor when all the time ...' She choked to a halt, unable to continue. They were standing glaring at each other, the room's atmosphere so highly charged that every sound seemed magnified, the rasp of each agitated breath, the crack of his knuckles as with fists clenched he fought for control.

'At the beginning of our acquaintance I was too involved with other, more pressing matters such as getting to know you better, striving to hold your interest. Later, when I became aware of your obsessive interest in money, of your arrogant assumption that with the power it bestows you could strip a man of his pride, his principles, and even of his will, I was too disgusted to argue the subject.'

A little of the hardness went from his voice and in its place she recognised a hint of pity which she found infuriating. 'I now realise that the fault was not one of character but of upbringing. You were born to riches, but no one had bothered to explain to you that if we make for ourselves a world that is ugly and miserable no person, however rich, can purchase anything other than misery and unhappiness. I know only too well the truth of that statement, for when you agreed to marry me I would have felt just as fortunate, just as enriched, if I had been a pauper. Which is why, conversely,' he admitted grimly, 'I now feel envious of a beggar.'

Silence fell between them, a silence full of such sadness Tara had to fight an urge to cry. Animosity had fled, the air no longer crackled but pulsated, time seemed to be holding its breath, waiting for her reaction. She found it impossible to make any reply while inwardly struggling with emotions of regret and suspicion, sorrow and anger, dislike and a confusing desire to rush into his arms. She sensed Falcon watching her closely and was relieved when he made no effort to touch her as quietly he urged:

'Our marriage could work, Tara, if you would allow it to continue the way it began. Deny it if you wish, but there is no way you can convince me that you were not as happy as I during our wonderful first night in Gozo. Many times since I have wakened in the night and reached out, hungry to feel once again your satin-smooth body held hard against mine, aching to relive the utter delight bestowed by shy, exploring lips, to hear small gasps of ecstasy that could not have been feigned, and to share the agonising thrill of ultimate submission.'

Her heart was torn in two by the reminder of that

night when she had been a traitor to herself and to
Aithne. It took massive effort of will, infinite courage, to instil contempt into her voice when she told
him, 'It astonishes me the way a situation can appear
so differently in someone else's eyes.' Fractionally,
she paused, wondering if vandals felt as she did just
before destroying some fragile work of art, knowing
that, once despoiled, it could never be replaced.
'My memory is not so unreliable as yours appar-
ently is—all I can recall of that night is violence,
disgust and rape.'

She did not lift her eyes from the floor, but knew
by his utter stillness that her thrust had penetrated
deeply through his armour of pride. A clock on the
wall ticked away long, painful seconds during which
she found herself wishing with all her heart that the
lie she had uttered as balm to her shame could have
been chilled into silence before passing her cold
lips.

He moved. Anticipating revenge, she jerked out
of his reach before realising that his intention had
merely been to show her to the door.

'*Don't do that!*' His dark eyes looked tortured as
he stressed through lips so grim they barely moved,
'Don't cower from me! In future, you will have no
need. I promise that never again will you be called
upon to endure the physical demands of marriage.
Not until,' she felt frozen to the spot, wondering
what qualification he was about to make, 'you come
to me of your own accord and tell me honestly:
"Falcon, I love you ..."'

It seemed a very long time before warm fingers of early morning light began creeping into her bedroom. Tara had felt none of the glow of triumph that was supposed to accompany victory, but during the long night she had consoled herself with the thought that at least she had achieved part of her aim by eliciting from Falcon a promise that she would suffer no more of his amorous advances. He still seemed adamantly opposed to divorce, yet how could he, a man whose word was binding, be expected to endure for ever a situation wherein he was bound by a vow of celibacy. His virile appetite was bound to be his downfall. Proof of infidelity gave easy access to divorce, but if the waiting proved too tedious she would have to think of a way to make him change his mind, and was one method of making his life so intolerable he would welcome any chance to be rid of her.

Bridget scowled her disapproval of one unwrinkled pillow when she entered the bedroom carrying a tray of early morning tea—set for two. Nor were her sharp eyes fooled by Tara's studied air of unconcern when, after adjusting the shutters to allow more light into the room, she returned to the bedside to observe, 'It's a fine thing when a man is driven by his wife's neglect into spending his honeymoon with her sister. They are breakfasting together now, planning some outing for the day; you'd better hurry and get ready before Aithne persuades him to leave without you.'

Tara avoided her eyes, wondering how much the sharp-eyed, keen-eared old woman actually knew and how much was mere guesswork. Deciding her remarks were best left ignored, Tara glanced at her watch, feigning surprise.

'Is that really the time? I had no idea it was so late.' She closed her eyes, shutting out Bridget's outraged face, and snuggled down into the bed. 'I feel lazy this morning. Just leave the tray, I'll have tea later when I'm feeling more rested.'

'It will get cold.' The terse ultimatum was accompanied by the rattle of spoons and china as the tray was thumped down on to a table.

'Then I'll ring for some fresh,' Tara replied, sweetly determined not to be riled, only to be brought almost to the brink when Bridget stalked out and slammed the bedroom door.

As soon as it was safe, she sat up and poured out the tea, prepared to linger upstairs until she was sure that Falcon and Aithne had left the house. She drained her cup, then sank back against the pillows intending to try to make up the sleep lost during hours of dark introspection when she had tossed and turned in her bed railing at the fate that had led her into marriage with a man she hated but who, in spite of her denials, remained the central character of a blissful memory, a man whose nearness could set her nerves rioting, whose eyes, when they met hers, often betrayed a hunger that stirred within the deep well of her body a matching desire to be devoured. She had moaned in half-sleep, trying to disperse his image from her mind, trying not to remember the touch of hands that had led her so tenderly into love, the excitement of his kisses, the shared whisperings, the ultimate bliss of two bodies locked in passion.

She was so steeped in misery she did not hear the tap upon her door and became conscious of Falcon's presence only when she looked up and saw him at the side of her bed.

'Get up, lazybones,' he teased, 'you've kept us waiting long enough!' There was no trace of decimated pride in the eyes that laughed down at her, no tension in the body that relaxed on to the side of her bed. He looked completely recovered, at ease in well-cut slacks and a casual shirt that left strong neck and bronzed forearms bare.

With a gesture that betrayed more than she intended, she pulled the bedcovers under her chin and turned her head aside. 'I'm tired, I prefer to stay here, if you don't mind.'

'But I do mind,' he insisted lightly. 'You will enjoy a day at the beach, the fresh air will do you good.'

'No, thank you,' she stubbornly refused. She felt the pressure of hands on either side of her body as he leant across, pinning her to the bed.

'You *will* come,' he told her silkily, 'even if I have to make you.'

'So much for your promises,' she flared. 'Last night you swore to leave me alone!'

'I did,' he agreed, 'but in only *one* respect.' He bent his head so that she was trapped by a deep, dark look of intent. 'I made no mention, if aggravated, of not getting you out of bed, stripping you, bathing you, dressing you and hauling you downstairs, by force if necessary. Unfortunately, you possess a tendency to arouse within me base instincts which hitherto I never knew existed. You will do as I say, Tara,' he growled softly, 'because you are perfertly well aware that if it should come to a fight not even a red-haired, fury-spitting she-cat can outmatch a tiger!'

Green eyes, glaring fury, took his measure, trying to judge whether or not the threat would be carried out. He withstood her scrutiny with ease, allowing a small smile to play around his lips as he waited for her reaction. But his indolent manner was contradicted by an intent gleam in eyes that did not waver from her face, and it was this glint that decided her that, for the first time in her life, she must submit to a man's will.

'On second thoughts,' she told him coolly, unwilling to concede defeat, 'I'd better accompany you, if only to protect Aithne.'

His brow furrowed. 'You are convinced that Aithne requires protection?'

'Of course; my naïve young sister is still in love with you. Knowing how easily she can be manipulated and also,' she stressed bitterly, 'how expertly you can manipulate, it would be foolish of me to allow her out of my sight.'

'Tara,' he sighed, sadly shaking his head, 'you have a very low opinion of me. Sometimes I wonder if it is myself in particular or men in general that you hate. Am I being made a scapegoat for the shortcomings of others? Traumas experienced in early childhood can ruin a person's adult life, and I believe that the only way to rid oneself of such effects is to literally re-live them. Some time, as a defenceless child, I suspect you were made to feel neglected and unloved; your cure will come about only when you are certain that you are wanted, deeply and sincerely,' his hand lifted to stroke the length of her cheek, 'and I don't mean just physically. You are a very lovable person—a sensitive plant protected by thorns.'

Tara was trying to rally her scattered senses in defence of an onslaught of charm when he took the wind from her sails by administering a brisk pat on her cheek before rising to his feet.

'Be as quick as you can,' he smiled at her from the doorway, 'we'll be waiting downstairs.'

She stared without moving long after he had gone. His change of mood was confusing, his impulses difficult to control—yet not half so difficult as her own!

CHAPTER EIGHT

THEY travelled by car to a lido, a private strip of beach reserved exclusively for the use of the island's social élite.

'I thought I'd visited every place of interest!' Aithne exclaimed, showing obvious approval of the miniature playground laid out to accommodate a dozen or so sun-loungers spread out beneath huge umbrellas of matted straw that were providing essential protection from the heat of the sun. A couple of speedboats bobbed at the water's edge with two bronzed young men in attendance, awaiting the appearance of the first water-skiing enthusiasts. At the top of steps leading down to the beach was a restaurant, and within convenient reach of the sun-worshippers was a large beached boat, its timbers gaily painted, having in place of sails a striped awning shading rows of bottles from the heat as well as protecting the man busily serving drinks from the novel bar. Young men, casually undressed in faded jeans cut short above the knee, hurried to serve trays of food, drink, ices and fruit to elegant women sporting the very latest fashions in beachwear and their escorts who, almost without exception, wore the jaded expressions of men tired out by constant chasing after the wealth essential to maintain their required standard of living.

'Why haven't I been brought here before?' Aithne questioned Falcon.

'Membership is limited to a small number,' he explained. 'Your friends, the de Marcos, have been on the waiting list for some time and should by now have achieved their aim. In fact, unless I'm very much mistaken,' he lifted a hand to shade his eyes, 'I think I see them over there!' As they made their way towards a couple waving madly to attract their attention, Falcon was greeted on all sides by parties obviously anxious to have him join them. Tara felt a slight liking for him when he politely declined the many invitations and continued ushering Aithne and herself towards the newcomers who had been left isolated on the very fringe of society.

'How glad I am to see you!' Dolores gasped when they reached her. 'Today is our first time here and we haven't been made to feel at all welcome. Though we're acquainted with most of these people,' she cast a look of disgust at the bodies littering the beach, 'they've made us feel like lepers! For a long time we've waited to be admitted into this exclusive circle, but I'm now beginning to wonder why we bothered.'

Her husband Mario, busy discussing with Falcon the best positions for the sun-loungers speedily provided by an attendant, turned merry eyes upon his disgruntled wife. 'Dolores, my pet, I'm certain you will never again need to complain about being left out. Have you not yet realised that, as the chosen companions of the Baron and Baroness Falzon, our name is now made! Every door on the island will be open to us, every exalted household will want us at its table.' They all burst out laughing at the expression of bemused incredulity on Dolores' face, causing many eyebrows to raise and many envious eyes to raise in their direction.

Only Tara was not amused; she found such snobishness intolerable, so was barely able to acknowledge fawning smiles as she and Aithne made their way towards gaily painted huts used as changing rooms.

'Do they consider their little set mankind!' she fumed. 'I have no time for cliques, especially toffee-nosed cliques!'

'Darling,' Aithne drawled, 'the path of social advancement is strewn with thin-skinned people. The de Marcos are a nice enough couple but nondescript, don't you think?'

Tara halted in her tracks, disgusted by her sister's disloyalty to a couple who had shown her nothing but kindness. 'How can you say such a thing! The de Marcos are our friends!'

Unmoved by the outburst, Aithne shrugged. 'How many friendships would endure if we each knew what our friends were saying about us in our absence? Don't be so intense, Tara, and for heaven's sake remember your position. You owe it to Falcon to be polite to these people, who are, after all, the only ones on the island worth cultivating.'

Tara stared at Aithne's disdainful features. 'At times,' she condemned her sister hardly, 'I wonder if I know you well, or not at all!'

She felt pleased, when rummaging in her bag,

that when choosing a bathing suit she had been impelled by an impulse to shock. The strait-laced Maltese were in for a surprise, she thought, easing her way into a one-piece suit of a design that was a roaring success on Continental beaches but which she felt sure would meet with disapproval in a country noted for its strict observance of convention. Taking a deep breath, she tossed her head and stepped outside to stroll with cat-like tread towards her unsuspecting companions. Surprised gasps accompanied her progress and the knowledge that her outfit was having the desired effect added an extra sparkle to her green eyes.

As she stepped up to her party and did a twirl before their startled eyes Falcon stirred. He had already changed and was lying face down letting the sun play upon his back. At the sound of concerted gasps he lifted his head, stared, then twisted upright on his lounger.

'Good lord ... !' He lapsed into stunned silence, staring his fill at a curvaceous body clad in a costume of yellow and black tiger stripes, smooth and tight as a second skin. The design was a dramatic, lifelike copy of a tiger pelt, but its greatest impact was contained within two glaring yellow eyes, each perfectly positioned, one covering each breast. Down the length of Tara's stomach, central to the eyes, ran a flat-bridged nose ending just below the navel in two flaring nostrils with, beneath these, a wide fanged mouth fringed with whiskers that curved from a cruel top lip and progressed around the back of her slinky hips. A pointed chin fitted exactly the natural vee formed by the meeting of her upper thighs.

'Purrfect!' Mario breathed, oblivious of his wife's scandalised eyes. 'Tell me, Falcon, are the contents as wild as the wrapping?'

Before he could reply Aithne broke in, a trifle sourly. 'My sister's temperament is such that she can be one minute playful as a kitten and the next tempestuous as the wild cat she is attempting to emulate.' Her lip curled, betraying chagrin at having her brief two-piece upstaged. 'I'm not sure whether I would care to wear anything so provocatively sexy.'

Falcon jumped to his feet and grabbed Tara by the wrist. 'I must discover if this she-cat likes water!' he grinned, then dragged her off towards the sea. He plunged straight in and began towing her into deeper water. She spluttered a protest, but it was ignored, so she held her breath and clung hard, determined that once she was released she would have her revenge. They were well beyond fear of observation when he began treading water and turned her round in his arms so that she was facing him. She glimpsed devilment in his eyes before his head descended, blotting out the sun, then his mouth covered hers in a kiss that drained the life from her limbs and sent heat searing through her body. She was still quaking when he deposited her in the shallows and turned to swim back out to sea, his laughter triumphant, audible only to her ears. Weak as the bedraggled kitten she resembled, she staggered out of the sea then made her way slowly up the beach. She had wanted to shock him, perhaps outrage, but had only succeeded in arousing within him the fierce instincts of a tiger lusting after its mate!

She had almost dried off, Falcon was still swimming, and Mario and Dolores had decided to attempt to water-ski, when Aithne's voice murmured in her ear, 'Tara, are you awake?'

She was lying flat, her back turned towards the sun, but she responded to the question by turning her head and lifting a drowsy eyelid. 'Just ...' She smothered a yawn.

'I've had no chance to talk to you since Father dropped his bombshell,' Aithne rushed on, her voice hard. 'The old fool has us well and truly scuppered! What are we going to do?'

'Economise, I suppose.' Tara was now wide awake. 'Sell off the estate and look for a small house somewhere. If Father hasn't exaggerated the state of his affairs, we may even have to find work.'

Aithne sent her an icy stare. 'Now you're being ridiculous! But *you* can afford to make light of the affair, having no doubt decided to stick tight to your rich husband. But what about me? I need money, and I need it now!'

Tara shot upright. Though there was no chance of their conversation being overheard she kept her voice low as, ignoring Aithne's innuendo, she declared, 'Father may be broke, but I'm certain he'll have sufficient spare cash to meet incidentals. Ask him for enough to cover your needs, he's not likely to quibble over a trifling sum.'

'The amount I need is hardly trifling. As a matter of fact,' Aithne gulped, 'it's rather frightening.'

Tara's brow furrowed. 'Are you trying to tell me you're in debt? If so, to whom ... ?'

She had never seen Aithne look quite so shaken. Proud of her matt complexion, she always took care to keep out of the sun, but lack of tan could not account for her ashen whiteness, nor for a bottom lip trembling like a child's.

'I've been very foolish,' Aithne confessed, then rushed to her own defence. 'Although I was hardly to know that we were about to lose all our money, was I? I owe five thousand pounds to the casino! I gambled and lost heavily during the weeks I spent here on holiday. When I explained my position and supplied proof of identity they allowed me a month's grace in which to return with the money. Naturally, I had to bide my time before approaching Father, hoping to catch him in a good mood, but he's been hopeless these past weeks, brooding, black-browed and filthy-tempered. News of your marriage sweetened him slightly, so when he suggested we pay you a visit I delayed mentioning my trouble, intending to tell him once we arrived on the island. I didn't know then that it was too late, that he was already bankrupt. You must help me, Tara!' Her blue eyes filled with tears as she pleaded, 'You *owe* it to me! Falcon has oodles of money, and besides, it's partly your fault that I'm in this mess, because if you hadn't played such a dirty trick it might have been *me* who landed a rich husband!'

Tara's set features masked the hurt inflicted by

Aithne's accusation. All her life she had considered her younger sister's interests before her own, yet all she had received in return were sulks and recriminations. Steeling herself against the adverse criticism she knew was about to come, she intoned stonily, 'I'm sorry, Aithne, but I can think of nothing, at the moment, that might help. I must repeat to you what I've already told Father. I will not be put under any obligation to Falcon; I want there to be no ties between us. Contrary to what you think, I'm more determined than ever to be free of him.'

'I can't deny that I'm pleased about that,' Aithne sniffed, 'but divorce takes time and I have to hand over the money before this week is up.'

'Then you'll have to throw yourself upon Father's mercy,' Tara sighed. 'Try not to worry, I'm certain that if we all put our heads together we'll think of some way of raising the money.'

But it was an appalling sum. Previously, the fact that Aithne had run up debts amounting to five thousand pounds would have caused her no more than a raised eyebrow; even O'Toole would have ranted and raved, but paid up, as he always had— she was only just beginning to realise how difficult life could be without a constant supply of money.

The sun was shining as hotly as ever, but for her the brightness had gone out of the day. When Falcon returned from his swim, looking invigorated and carefree, shaking water from his sea-tousled hair, he received no reaction to his taunting grin. His eyes narrowed. Taking a seat directly facing her, he directed a searching look.

'What's wrong, Tara?'

He was surprisingly sensitive to her moods. She had been trying to project an air of calm, yet she knew that his probing eyes had penetrated her façade. Sensing that it would be useless to pretend, she fell back upon woman's oldest excuse.

'I have a slight headache—too much sun, perhaps.'

He hesitated, his glance sliding towards Aithne who was lying prone and seemingly unaware of their conversation. He seemed disinclined to believe her, but to her relief he did not argue.

'In that case, we will return home. Gather up your things while I look for the de Marcos to tell them we are leaving.'

Mario and Dolores were disappointed, but became slightly mollified when as they were taking their leave Falcon extended an invitation. 'I intend, very shortly, to arrange a gathering of friends and acquaintances to whom Tara has yet to be introduced. As our house in Valetta does not have rooms sufficiently large to accommodate large numbers the party will have to be held in the Palazzo Falzon to which we shall soon be returning. We shall, of course, send you an invitation which I hope you will be able to accept?'

'We most certainly will!' Dolores clapped her hands with delight. 'Just try keeping us away!'

During the drive back to Valetta Tara sensed his puzzled eyes glancing first towards her own and then towards Aithne's tense features. She tried to lighten the atmosphere by making conversation, but her effort fell flat. Aithne refused to join in; she had, it seemed, fallen into one of the sulky, morose moods Tara knew and dreaded.

Some of the pressure lifted when finally she entered the house and headed straight for her bedroom. After a shower and a change of clothing she felt much better, but her brow was still furrowed when, after slipping into a loose-fitting negligee of pale green, she wandered into the sitting-room of the suite and dropped on to the couch. She would, she fretted, have to have a long talk with her father. It was impossible, without his guidance to even guess at the value of their remaining assets. She concentrated hard, trying to evaluate her own personal possessions, and discovered, to her slight surprise, that she owned very few items valuable enough to be turned into cash. Her mother had disliked jewellery, therefore there had been none for her daughters to inherit. Because of Tara's love of outdoor pursuits, her own purchases had been confined mostly to livestock—a quiet, beautiful mare and a young Arab stallion whose temperament had just about begun to respond to her patient handling before she had left for Malta. She suspected that both animals would be regarded as part of her father's collateral. Both she and Aithne had clothes in plenty, but again, these were hardly realisable assets, therefore they could be discounted. Five thousand pounds! The amount drummed into her brain. How on earth was she to find a sum which, the more she thought of it, the more unattainable it became?

Not even Falcon's entry into the room penetrated her worried absorption. She started when he spoke her name and looked up to see him carrying a casket of tooled leather which when he sat down, he placed on the couch between them.

'You seemed depressed,' he explained casually. 'I've brought you a present to cheer you up.'

'You shouldn't have bothered.' Her reply was brief yet not ungracious.

'Open it,' he urged, turning a gold key in a miniature lock before pushing the box towards her.

Reluctantly she lifted the lid, then blinked when sunlight fell upon the contents, firing them with a breathtaking burst of rainbow-coloured sparkles. 'How lovely!' she breathed, fingering one by one each item as she took it from the velvet-lined case. There were earrings of fine gold moulded into the shape of female heads, two Egyptian scarab rings, a necklace composed of linked rosettes hung with beads of lapis lazuli, a cameo carved in onyx, a circular gold brooch set with garnets and another of seed pearls, and an assortment of gold pendants delicately modelled in forms of animals and birds —a pelican, a swan, a horse, a dolphin, with eyes, hooves and beaks picked out in different coloured stones.

'None of these pieces is exceptionally valuable,' Falcon shrugged, looking pleased by her reaction. 'Some time, I must show you our collection of family jewellery which is at present housed in the vaults of a bank, but meanwhile you may make use of these baubles as costume jewellery. They are possessed of a certain sentimental value, but their loss would cause me no great anxiety.'

His attitude was casual, yet she suspected that the jewellery was of greater value than he had implied. Hastily, she returned the pieces to their case and closed the lid. 'Please,' she pushed it towards him, 'take them back. I don't want to be responsible for their safe keeping.'

The smile faded from his lips. 'Are you genuinely concerned, or are you merely making an excuse? Jewellery, regardless of its value, possesses certain sentimental and romantic connotations—are you afraid that by accepting such a present you will be made to feel somehow committed?'

'No,' she assured him swiftly, 'I hadn't given that aspect of the matter a thought.'

'Then I insist that you take them,' once more the case was pushed in her direction. 'As I said before, they are of no great value. Except ...' he corrected, leaning forward to raise the lid, 'this one piece which was a favourite of my mother's. It ought to have been returned to the bank after last being worn, but must somehow have been overlooked.' He lifted out of the case a gold pendant shaped into the image of a falcon with outspread wings. Set into the body of the bird was a large gem, pulsating red, encircled by white, square-cut stones with the glitter of ice. A band clasped around the bird's highly-arched neck sparkled with the same green light as two sharp eyes sunk into a gold head.

'It ... it looks costly,' Tara choked, very conscious that the qualities of strength, power, pride and cruelty inherent within the bird of prey were similar to those endowed upon the family that had adopted its name.

'Enchanting ...' he murmured, his attention upon tiny tendrils of hair that had earlier escaped the protection of her shower cap and were now clinging damply against the curve of her neck. With head bent, engrossed in examining her treasure trove, she received no warning of danger before he pounced swiftly, branding a fiery kiss of possession against her neck.

'I am a nape-of-the-neck maniac,' he murmured, 'did I ever tell you that? While other men are attracted by slender legs or shapely breasts I find myself drawn irresistibly towards this cool, secret hollow of seduction.'

Furiously she jumped up, spilling a cascade of jewels at her feet. 'I might have guessed you would expect some sort of payment!' she accused angrily.

Resentment flared in his eyes, but with great effort of will he swallowed back the denial on his lips and contented himself with a softly-growled, fairly mild condemnation. 'Damn you, Tara! Rewards come only after victory, and I have not achieved victory—yet.'

CHAPTER NINE

NEITHER Aithne nor O'Toole seemed conscious of the same enchantment Tara had experienced the first time she entered the M'Dina, the Silent City whose walls protected all that was left of the mystique and glory of ancient Malta. The Palazzo itself, however, impressed them greatly. O'Toole especially could not disguise his envy as he walked from room to room, his footsteps resounding more and more rapidly upon marble floors as his interest quickened.

In the huge, stately ballroom he halted to examine frescoes depicting episodes from great battles, then continued more slowly, stopping every now and then to scan the many portraits hung upon the walls.

'Holbein, Fedu, Van Loo ...' he murmured, mentally tabulating the worth of the old masters, but as they progressed towards the Tapestry Chamber crammed with superb antiques, its walls lined with tapestries depicting exotic hunting scenes, then to the Armoury housing hundreds of fine examples of arms and weapons dating back to the early sixteenth century, he gave up.

There was indictment in his look, and in Aithne's, when he chided Tara, 'Falzon's wealth is incalculable! You knew he had all this,' he waved an encompassing hand, 'yet you still refused to approach him for help? The price of one picture alone would be sufficient to get us out of trouble.'

'He would never sell——' she gasped.

'He would have no need,' her father interrupted. 'I was merely attempting to illustrate the fact that a man of such wealth would consider the sum we need less than paltry. He has far more than he needs —yet we have nothing!' Hearing the statement from his own lips seemed to bring home to him the enormity of the problem he faced. Wealth is relative. Amongst men of his own standing he had been considered fortunate to possess a large family home, tenanted farms, a more than comfortable income accrued from investments laid down by ancestors far shrewder than himself, and the residue of a fortune left by his wife who herself had been the only child of a wealthy family. But compared with the Baron he felt as a gnome against a giant. The realisation provoked an unjustifiable resentment which was evident in the hard stare he inflicted upon Tara.

'It's most unfair that one man should be allowed to possess so much when others have so little. He's duty bound to help us! After all, we're now part of his family.'

Tara had never felt such contempt for anyone as she did for O'Toole at that moment. 'When you had plenty,' she glared, 'how much did you give away?'

'I never hesitated to help any friend in trouble,' he blustered. 'No one ever came to me for help and was turned away. Please ask him, Tara,' he began to coax.

'*No!* I will not beg!' She stamped her foot to emphasise that she meant what she said. 'We may have lost our money, but I insist we retain our self-respect!' The silence of the great hall echoed with the appeal in her voice when she pleaded, 'Please, Father, don't let's argue, we must try to be constructive, we must sit down together and weigh up our assets. Things may not be as bad as they appear. After all, there's the house, the estate, the livestock alone——'

'All of which,' he cut in hardly, 'are due to come under the auctioneer's hammer in exactly two days from now, *including*,' he stressed cruelly, 'your beloved horses. Considering the amount of care and affection you lavished upon those animals, I would have thought you would be prepared to go to any lengths to keep them.'

She stepped back, her eyes anguished.

'As soon as that ... ?' she faltered.

'Just two days,' he affirmed with a curt nod. 'That's all the time you have left in which to reject your stubborn pride and to reconsider your attitude towards your extremely wealthy husband.'

Blissfully unaware of the pressures being brought to bear upon her charge, Bridget fussed happily around Tara's bedroom, unpacking her belongings, placing clothes on to hangers, then transferring them almost reverently into wardrobes so vast she had to stand on tip-toe to reach the rails.

'What a fortunate girl you are!' She stepped

back to cast admiring eyes around the bedroom
which she fondly imagined Tara would be sharing
with Falcon. It was very different from the room
in Gozo, with its cupids, entwined hearts and other
symbols of nuptial bliss. This room, again one of a
suite designed to accommodate the master and mistress of the house, conjured, with the help of
heavily-carved furniture, a huge canopied four-
poster bed, and velvet covers and curtains of sombre
green, an ambience of dignified elegance. A room
which had no doubt struck awe into the hearts of
many generations of Falzon brides, the huge bed
a fitting monument to the number of Falzon heirs
who had been conceived and delivered in its depths.

Tara's eyes shuddered from its bulk, knowing
her head would toss uneasily on pillows of pristine
lawn, knowing that within its embrace her solitary
nights would be tormented by thoughts of what
might have been—of what had already been.

'We had quite a time setting this room to rights,'
Bridget prattled on. Seemingly, without either help
or encouragement from Tara, she had become en-
sconced within the bosom of Falcon's domestic
household. 'Maria was telling me that this suite
has not been used for many years—not since the
Baron's parents were alive to share it. It had not
been allowed to fall into a state of neglect, of course,
but it did require a thorough cleaning. The Baron's
father was killed during the last year of the war.
The news that his ship had been sunk was given
to his wife only weeks before her son was due to
be born. Maria swears that the shock of her hus-

band's death was so great she was left without the
will to live. She almost died during childbirth, but
they managed to pull her through although she remained an invalid for the rest of her days. So you
see, from infancy the Baron has felt the burden of
responsibility. As soon as he was old enough to
reason he became his mother's shadow, trying to
make up to her for the unhappiness he sensed within her. They say he adored her, her welfare was
always his first consideration right up until her
death three years ago.'

Painfully touched by the image in her mind of a
small boy trying to demonstrate his love yet being
made conscious always of being rated second-best to
his dead father, Tara turned on Bridget with a flash
of temper.

'How dare you encourage the Baron's servants to
gossip about his affairs? You disappoint me, Bridget,
I thought you knew better!'

Offended to the depths of her being, Bridget drew
drew herself erect, then disciplined a trembling
mouth to form the dignified reply. 'Paul and Maria
do not consider themselves to be mere servants.
Having been part of the Falzon household for more
than fifty years, they feel they're entitled to worry
about the Baron's welfare, to rejoice in his happiness, to claim a status nearer to that of fond aunt
and uncle. They recognised the same quality in myself,' when her voice broke into a quiver she
breathed deeply, then recovered sharply, 'and
treated me accordingly—not as a gossiping servant,
but as a concerned, respected member of a family.'

'Oh, Bridget!' With a cry of remorse Tara flung down the comb she had been twisting through her fingers and ran to put her arms around the old woman's shoulders. Burying her head on her shoulder, she pleaded, 'Please forgive me, I love you dearly—you know that—I hate myself for speaking those cruel words. Promise me you'll forget them, Bridget,' she begged, tightening the pressure of her arms around the old woman's still stiff body. 'I don't know what's wrong with me lately, I've become so irritable, so confused, ever since ...' She hesitated, not quite certain when.

'Since your marriage to the Baron,' Bridget relented, returning her hug, 'which is not surprising considering that, from the day your heart prompted you into promising that you would love, honour and obey him, your wayward nature decreed that you should do exactly the opposite. Make peace with him and you will make peace with yourself, alannah.' Then, feeling reinstated to the position of confidante and friend, she questioned with asperity, 'How much longer do you intend to fight him? Is it so terribly hard to face up to the truth, to admit to yourself that you are in love with him?'

When Bridget had left the room, huffed by the tacit and most unladylike response her remark had received, Tara slumped into a chair, racked by the tension of prolonged pressure. Everyone, it seemed, was bent upon breaking her will—Aithne and her father because they were in desperate need of money; Bridget because her sentimental old heart had convinced her that simply by wishing dreams could be made to come true, and most of all Falcon who, for reasons she could not fathom, had embarked upon a campaign of deliberate torment. But before any semblance of peace could be achieved, Aithne swept into the room.

'Oh, no ... !' Tara groaned inwardly, preparing once again to marshal her defences.

But Aithne did not immediately begin her attack. Instead, she began wandering around the room, idly fingering various ornaments, but with such an air of abstraction it was clear that her mind was on other things.

'Where is Falcon?' she asked eventually. 'I haven't seen him since breakfast.'

'He was called away—some urgent business at the winery, I think. He left a message with Paul that he didn't expect to be back until this evening.'

'Working! On his honeymoon...?' Aithne quizzed lightly. 'But then,' her glance swung suddenly to Tara's face, 'I don't suppose he considers it to be much of a honeymoon.'

'Perhaps not,' Tara replied briefly, reaching out for the jewel box that had been left on a nearby table in an effort to hide her agitation.

'What's that?' Aithne pounced. 'I don't remember seeing it before.'

Glad of any excuse to steer the conversation into less turbulent channels, Tara raised the lid. 'Some trinkets Falcon thought I might like to wear as costume jewellery—inexpensive, but nice, don't you think?'

Aithne carried the box across to the window

where the light could fall upon its contents. Tara relaxed, thinking her ploy had worked, then stiffened to attention when, as she was sorting through the jewellery, Aithne suddenly shot, 'You didn't answer my question. Have you slept with Falcon?' She swung round just in time to see colour rushing into Tara's cheeks. 'You *have*!' she accused harshly. 'Don't try to deny it, the truth is written on your face.'

'Not from choice!' Tara blurted, then, made angry by her sister's insensitivity, continued in a more dignified tone, 'I was treated in exactly the same way, I imagine, as you were yourself. I need hardly remind you that the Baron's mixed blood has endowed him with the arrogance of a Spanish grandee, the thieving instincts of a corsair, and an Arab's contemptuous belief that woman's sole purpose in life is to pander to the pleasures of man.'

She waited for some sign of sympathy, a show of concern, but was shocked when Aithne rounded, obviously incensed, 'In other words, you belong to him! Once more I've been left with only crumbs to peck—I have only memories while you have the pleasure of feeling his kisses upon your lips; I can only imagine his touch while you can revel in his caresses!'

'*Stop it!*' Driven towards the very edge of endurance, Tara clapped her hands over her ears. 'I don't want to hear another word!'

'Too bad! You're just going to *have* to listen!'

But Tara had had enough. Evading the sight of Aithne's condemning eyes, of features contorted with a jealousy that was almost akin to hatred, she ran past, wrenched open the door, and fled.

She ran blindly, without sense of direction. During the few hours she had spent in the Palazzo before her wedding there had been no time for exploration, but instinct led her towards the back of the house where a blast of perfume-laden air beckoned her towards an archway leading into a sunken garden, an arbour of beauty within which blossoms spilled from tubs down the length of high sun-warmed walls, a fountain tinkled into a shallow basin filled with darting, multi-coloured fish, and trees cast a blessed mantle of shade across a seat fashioned out of porous golden stone carved and scrolled so many centuries earlier that when she sat down and began tracing the outline of a Falzon crest pieces crumbled away beneath her shaking fingers.

She stared with hurt, unhappy eyes at a broken falcon's wing. How easily it had disintegrated! How strange, that something one imagined was strong and indestructible could collapse at the slightest pressure. She had thought herself part of a family united not only by ties of blood but also of loyalty and deep affection, but that, too, had crumbled. She struggled with the bitter hurt of her family's defection—Aithne's dislike, her father's anger, even Bridget's gentle resentment, had all been brought about by the intrusion into their lives of one arrogant, unscrupulous man.

She looked outwardly composed when, hours later, she went down to dinner. Yet her nerves tensed when she entered the room and saw that only her father and Aithne were present. O'Toole was surprisingly affable.

'Would you like me to pour you a drink before dinner, my dear,' he beamed, 'or shall we go straight in? When I finished talking with Falcon earlier today he told me that if he was delayed and hadn't returned by the time dinner was due to be served we were not to wait but to start without him. Which is a relief, I must admit, for I can hardly wait to sample yet another excellent meal.'

'You were talking to Falcon?' Tara eyed her father suspiciously as he escorted her into the dining room. 'About what?'

'Man's talk, my dear. Nothing you should worry your pretty head about.'

Having plenty to occupy her mind, she ignored his facetious reply and tried during dinner to carry on a normal conversation. But Aithne would not co-operate; Tara was conscious always of her sullen, brooding presence and was also aware, much to her own annoyance, that her eyes, of their own volition, kept straying towards the empty chair at the head of the table.

O'Toole drank his way steadily through dinner and afterwards, with the air of a man completely content with his world, settled himself into a comfortable armchair with a glass of brandy in his hand and a bottle from which to replenish it placed handily on a nearby table. When Aithne excused herself and went up to her room Tara sat down opposite her father, deciding that this rare interlude of privacy should not be wasted.

'Father,' she probed delicately, 'shouldn't you be in Ireland looking after your affairs? There's sure to be documents to sign, problems to be resolved, and if Caliph and Traleen,' she choked on the names of her two beloved horses, 'are to be sold I can't bear the thought of them going to just anyone —couldn't you——'

'They've already been sold,' he told her, benignly insensitive to the lash inflicted by his words, 'and to a buyer who will meet with your complete approval. So relax, enjoy what you have, and don't worry, everything is going beautifully.'

'Don't worry!' she flared, jumping to her feet, wanting to shake sense into the man indolently drinking brandy while everything most dear to them was being threatened by the auctioneer's hammer. 'How can you sit there full of complacency and tell me not to worry when ... when ...' She broke off when tears welled into her eyes. To be destitute was bad enough, but her greatest heartbreak was the knowledge that never again would she hear a soft whinny of greeting from the gentle-eyed mare she had owned and loved since childhood, or know the exhilaration of being carried fast as the wind upon the back of the proud young stallion that had consistently refused to respond to anyone's voice but her own. Traleen was too old to be of interest to any rider other than one requiring a placid mount, but Caliph's prancing hooves, flaring nostrils and

disdainfully tossing mane would attract many
bidders. In the wrong hands his proud spirit could
be broken—but only after prolonged and painful
battle.

When O'Toole's hand reached out once more for
the bottle she turned away with a gasp of despair.
'I'm going to my room,' she mumbled, hating his
casual, unfeeling attitude.

'Do that, my dear,' he replied so affably she could
have struck him. 'I'll sit here and wait until Falcon
returns.'

As she mounted the stairs her mind vaguely registered the slamming of a door followed by the rev-
ving of a car as it accelerated through the empty
streets of the M'Dina. She half hoped Bridget might
be in the sitting-room; she needed to talk to someone who would understand the magnitude of her
sorrow. Bridget had once chided: 'You're wasting
the best years of your life on those creatures, it's
babies you should be fussing over, not a couple of
dumb animals!' Then had been rendered speechless when lightheartedly she had replied, 'Of the
many attributes possessed by animals, Bridget, the
greatest of all is their dumbness!'

But when she reached the sitting-room Bridget
was nowhere to be seen. She slumped into a chair,
then a second later jumped to her feet and began
prowling the room, wishing she had remained downstairs, feeling that in her restless, over-emotional
state even O'Toole's company was preferable to
none at all. She halted suddenly, her attention
caught by the jewellery box standing slightly open

with a bright object protruding from beneath the lid. She opened it wide, impatient of Aithne's careless handling, then began automatically to rearrange the contents that had been left in an untidy jumble. Almost halfway through she stiffened, then began rummaging frantically through the remainder, searching for the piece she had sensed was missing —the item that Falcon had indicated was of more value than the rest. After five tense minutes she had to accept the fact that it had gone—the jewelled falcon carrying a blood-red stone upon its breast, the piece of which he was especially fond because it had been a favourite of his mother's!

Where could it have gone? For half an hour she searched the room, turning over every cushion, crawling on her knees to search every inch of carpet, rifling every drawer, unwilling to admit that the piece was nowhere in the room. She sank into a chair, her brow wrinkling with the effort of trying to recall when she had last seen it. Aithne had been weighing it in her palm, eyeing it with intense interest, just before their row had erupted. Might she have thrust her fist into her pocket, forgetting, in the heat of the moment, what it contained?

She ran out of the room and down the passageway to Aithne's bedroom. After knocking and receiving no reply, she pushed open the door and stepped inside an empty room. Obviously Aithne had gone out—but where? Something clicked inside her brain, reminding her of the small disturbance she had heard while making her way upstairs, noises which she now realised had been those of a taxi picking up a passenger outside the Palazzo. She did not hesitate. There was no time for doubting, for feeling ashamed of harbouring unfounded suspicions. Grabbing a wrap from her room, she ran downstairs to Falcon's study where with shaking fingers she telephoned for a taxi.

It took a long, agonising twenty minutes to arrive and an equally long time to reach her destination. Her agitation was obvious as, without giving the driver time to assist her, she wrenched open the door and flung out of the taxi when it drew up outside the casino. She had never before visited the huge, internationally-known casino that was the island's pride. A flight of shallow stone steps led up to an imposing façade strewn with coloured lights. 'Wait for me, please!' she gasped to the driver, then ran up the steps and through an impressive doorway.

Once inside she found her way barred by a counter behind which a man was suavely presiding.

'May I have your entrance fee?' he requested politely. 'And would you please sign your name in this book?'

She scrabbled in her bag for the required sum, then without thinking signed 'Tara O'Toole' in the ledger he pushed towards her. A uniformed attendant then indicated that she should follow him, then led her, her heart thumping, her mouth dry, into a room as large as a ballroom that was packed with people crowding around a dozen or so tables each attended by a croupier. Harsh overhead lights beamed down upon faces whose intent, robot-fixed stares caused her a shudder. With eyes fastened upon the baize-topped tables they distributed their chips, then waited, their only reaction to either winning or losing showing in a slight tensing or relaxing of tight facial muscles.

Tara pushed her way through the crowded room searching for Aithne, yet desperately hoping that she would not be present. It was at the last, no-limit table that she saw her sister's fair head bent over several piles of high-value chips. She was seated between two men, Orientals, with calm inscrutable faces, who seemed to have hit a winning streak. Aithne, in a state of high excitement, was obviously following their lead, watching carefully while they placed their bets, then following suit with an equal amount even though their piles of chips were far superior to her own. One of the men began piling chips upon a chosen number, unmoved by the fact that he was about to gamble hundreds of pound upon one spin of the roulette wheel, his eyes beneath slanting lids betraying no hint of emotion as he sat back and waited until all bets had been placed.

As Tara watched, horrified, she saw Aithne hesitate, then, even as she breathed: 'Oh, no, Aithne, *don't* ... !' push forward the whole of her chips, indicating to the croupier that she wanted her bet to be placed upon number eleven, the same as that chosen by her neighbour. When the wheel began to spin Tara closed her eyes and prayed that when the small white ball had ceased its tantalising dance it would choose to fall into the space marked number eleven. When its clicking progress slowed, then finally ceased, she dared not look.

'Numéro huit ...!' the croupier intoned, confirming her worst fears. Number eight had won!

'Tara! What are you doing here?' She opened dazed eyes and stared into Aithne's frightened face.

'Looking for you,' she replied through lips that felt bloodless. 'You must have lost hundreds of pounds on that last game—where did you get your stake money?'

For once, Aithne seemed concerned about the consquences of her action. Grasping Tara by the arm, she pleaded with stricken eyes, 'Please believe me, Tara, I didn't mean to gamble. I was feeling so fed up I just had to get out of the house and decided to come here solely as a spectator, to while away a couple of hours. Then as I was watching, I became aware that those two Chinese were having a fantastic run of good luck. I dug my hands into my pockets, knowing that if I had just one pound to spare I could share in their good fortune, and it was then that I discovered ...' she faltered.

'The golden falcon,' Tara concluded wearily.

Miserably, Aithne nodded. 'It's not unusual for the rich clientele to use pieces of jewellery as collateral if ever they run short of money. Honestly, Tara, my intention was to redeem it once I'd won sufficient money for my own stake, but I became reckless when my winnings began piling up and I told myself that if I continued I would win enough both to redeem the falcon and to pay off my debt. And it would have happened,' she finished, bitterly regretful, 'if my run of luck hadn't run out with that very last bet.'

It was neither the time nor the place to deliver a lecture on the folly of gambling with money one could not afford to lose. Aithne had been criminally foolish, but at that moment all Tara wanted was to get away from the casino. She began bundling her towards the exit, but just as they were about to step outside a man stepped in front of them to voice a polite request.

'Miss O'Toole, would you please accompany me to our office, one of our directors would like to speak with you?'

Miss O'Toole, he had said, but with his eyes upon them both. Tara pushed Aithne towards the door. 'Leave this to me,' she hissed, 'you go home, there's a taxi waiting.'

Her legs were quaking as she was ushered along a silent passageway. After knocking upon a door and being bidden to enter the man pushed it open, then stepped aside, leaving her to enter alone. For a second she found it hard to focus in the dim interior of a room in darkness except for a lamp shining directly down on to a desk behind which a man's shadowy form was seated. She stepped forward. 'If it's about the jewellery, I can explain——' she began.

'Can you, Tara?' The figure leant forward until the beam of light was shining upon his face and upon the blood-red breast of the falcon cupped in his palm.

'Falcon ...!' her voice trailed into nothingness

as with frozen horror she stared at the man whose voice was a reflection of his face—hard-set and grey with weariness.

'If you were in need of money, why didn't you say so?' He sounded almost sad. 'I think I could have forgiven your bartering any of my possessions, other than this one.'

If he had ranted and raved, if he had threatened punishment, she could have weathered the experience, but this glimpse of naked hurt, the knowledge that he thought her capable of disposing of an item she knew he treasured, was too much for her thrashed emotions.

'Please,' she pleaded on a broken whisper, 'will you take me home?'

She was relieved that the drive along narrow, twisting roads kept his hands and eyes fully occupied, but unhappy that his contempt of her was such he could not, as yet, trust himself to speak. When the car drew up outside the Palazzo she jumped out and without a backward glance ran inside, straight upstairs, and into her bedroom. For a long time she remained with her back pressed against her locked door, straining her ears for the sound of vengeful footsteps, then was gradually able to relax when it became obvious that explanations and punishment were to be deferred.

She dragged her weary body into the bathroom and peeled off her clothes. The episode had left her feeling unclean; never in her life had her honesty been questioned, never had she been subjected to the sight of disgust in another person's eyes. She turned on the shower, then stepped beneath the warm, needle-sharp spray, closing sliding glazed doors behind her. She was enjoying the tingling warmth of water on her face when with shocking force the doors of the cubicle were thrust apart, setting the glass shuddering. With outrageous aplomb, Falcon eyed her nakedness. He had shrugged off his jacket and tie and left his shirt undone to the waist. His black hair was ruffled as if, during angry, silent debate, it had been run through with impatient fingers. Too late, Tara remembered that in his room was a doorway giving access to the bathroom.

Her flight had left him with time to think. Before, he had seemed merely sad, but after reflecting upon her treachery he had become enraged and vengeful. All this was reflected in the cold, intolerant raking of his eyes.

Instinctively, she lifted her hands to cover her breasts, a move so abortive he speared a look of grim derision.

'You protect your virtue as if it were your only coin,' he grated savagely. 'To look at you, one would never imagine that you do a brisk trade in deceit!'

Regardless of the hissing spray, he stepped inside the cubicle. In seconds his shirt was plastered against his chest and arms so that powerful, knotted muscles were outstanding. Within the confined space she was pressed hard against him, so that there was no way she could escape the fire and anger of his punishing kiss. Water rained down upon their heads as, in a state of outraged shock, she clung to him, gasping for breath as water lashed her face and stung against a body that had suddenly begun to burn. Such audacity was typical of the man who, all his life, had merely reached out and taken anything he wanted. His unexpected appearance, the swiftness of his attack, set her senses reeling. Like a shipwrecked kitten she clung to him as waves of emotion buffeted her traitorous body.

As he continued inflicting his anger upon her bruised lips she sensed his rage subsiding, giving way to a rising tide of desire, a desire which she was shamefully forced to share.

'Tara!' he husked, his voice, his hands, his whole body communicated desperate need. 'Put me out of my misery! For the love of heaven, say those three small words!

It would have been so easy to succumb to the mad flare of ecstasy aroused by caressing hands laying claim to every vulnerable inch of her. Three words: '*I love you*', would be enough to release him from his promise and herself from self-imposed bondage. Would it be so wrong—her mind raced in time with throbbing pulses—to give in to passion even though the man to whom she clung was a ruthless, skilful expert who had begun learning of woman's weaknesses at his mother's knee and had continued to enlarge upon and to exploit such knowledge at the expense of her gullible sex?

The reminder shocked her to the surface of sanity, jarring enough strength into her arms to push him away.

'No!' she cried, tormented by the pain of prolonged pleasure. 'If it should take me for the rest of my life, I will repay all that I owe you—*but not this way!*'

CHAPTER TEN

'FALCON, I should like to see over the winery, will you take me there today?' Looking very appealing in a navy and white peasant blouse teamed with a red skirt so full it swirled around her legs as she walked, Aithne posed against a trellis of climbing roses, red as her skirt, well aware that the effect was devastating.

They had just enjoyed breakfast served upon a terrace paved with sun-splashed tiles, its length lined by a balustrade along which stone urns crammed with flowers spilled rivulets of sweetly-perfumed blossoms on to the floor. Falcon pushed aside his coffee cup and smiled at Aithne.

'Certainly, if that is what you wish.' He glanced at Tara, whose expression was hidden by a wing of red hair as she bent to tempt the advance of a timid sparrow with strewn crumbs. As she leant a little too far, the bird, in a flurry of panic, took flight.

'Timid creature,' he drawled, his eyes upon her face, 'how mortifying to feel that one has to forgo the plum because one lacks the courage to shake the tree.' When she did not respond with so much as a blush his tone became impatient. 'Are we to enjoy the pleasure of your company today?' he jarred. 'Or have you yet more pressing matters that require your attention?'

It was a sarcastic reference to the fact that for the past three days she had avoided his company. On one pretext or another she had refused to leave the Palazzo, but she knew that her excuses had begun to wear thin as his tolerance.

'Oh, leave her alone!' Aithne coaxed, her smile complacent. Things were going very much to plan —her plan. For three days she had revelled in Falcon's exclusive company while he had taken her on a tour of the island, showing her places out of bounds to ordinary tourists, dining in restaurants where proprietors had rushed to serve them, making her feel that she was an honoured and favoured guest. The days had passed in a whirl. Falcon, though often morose, had seemed to want to cram as much activity as possible into the hours they had shared. At her insistence, they had ridden in a *karrozzin*, a funny little horse-drawn cab unique to the island, that had transported them, beneath a sky filled with glorious colour, along a sea-front road where they had watched in silence the slow demise of a Mediterranean sun dipping below the far horizon. Falcon had scoffed, but given in to her pleading to be allowed a trip around the grand harbour in a gaily painted *dghajsa*, the Maltese equivalent of a gondola, with the eye of Osiris, God of the Underworld, painted upon its elegant bow to ward off the evil eye.

His eyes held a similar satanic warning as coldly he prompted, 'Well, Tara, have you decided?'

To Aithne's dismay her sister responded with uncharacteristic lack of fire. 'Very well,' she shrugged, 'if you insist.'

'Good,' he replied tersely, 'I'll telephone the manager to let him know that we are coming.'

Bridget showed her delight as she helped her to dress for the outing. 'And about time, too,' she fussed, 'you've moped about long enough.' She reached into the wardrobe for a pretty silk dress patterned with tiny, pastel-shaded flowers and frowned when Tara shook her head, indicating her choice of tailored slacks and a collarless checked shirt, which instead of tucking into the waistband, she left hanging loosely around her hips.

'You're not going to meet your husband's employees wearing that!' Bridget exploded. 'I can't help wishing that, just this once, you would follow Aithne's example and dress properly. Compared with her you'll look like an urchin tagging along under duress!'

Which was exactly how Tara did feel as listlessly she made her way outside to the waiting car. Aithne was already seated in the passenger seat next to Falcon, so, ignoring her pleased smile and Falcon's raised eyebrows, she climbed into the back and slumped down upon the seat. His mouth tightened at her show of apathy, but he steeled himself to silence and strove, unsuccessfully, to hide his annoyance.

The winery was situated in the centre of a small industrial town made up of narrow streets filled with the comings and goings of traffic connected with various light industries. Lorries piled high with crates of bottles, their doors printed with the sign of the Falzon Winery passed in clouds of dust, and on the quayside of a small harbour wine was being loaded in bulk into the hold of a waiting ship. At the approach to the winery a gate attendant manipulated a mechanical barrier, then waved acknowledgement when they passed through into a yard containing more lorries being loaded with crates of bottles labelled with the trademark of the House of Falzon.

'Everything he owns has to be stamped with his seal of possession,' Tara registered bitterly, thinking back to the moment, a few days previously, when his sharp eyes had noted the absence of her wedding ring. Her fingers had been enclosed in a grip tight as his anger, as he had demanded, 'Where is your ring?'

She had stared vacantly at her naked finger, not daring to admit that she considered the ring a symbol of bondage and that she loathed its touch upon her skin. 'In my bedroom—I must have forgotten to replace it,' she had stammered the weak excuse, inwardly appalled at the absence of spirit which at one time would have flared into violent life at the least hint of censure.

'Fetch it,' he had commanded, 'and in future wear it always.'

'As a mark of possession?' she had sneered.

'As an indication of commitment,' he had replied quietly, his anger marshalled, 'to the vows we shared.'

As they stepped from the car a beaming man approached them. 'This is John Manduca, my manager,' Falcon introduced him. 'John, meet the Baroness Falzon and her sister, Miss Aithne O'Toole.'

The manager bowed pleasantly over each of their hands. 'Delighted to make your acquaintance, Baroness, and to have the opportunity of showing you our winery, I'm certain you will find it interesting. And you, too, Miss O'Toole. If you will come this way,' he waved a hand, 'we will begin at the beginning.'

Tara was surprised to discover housed within ancient buildings the very latest in modern machinery.

'The first process in wine production is the pressing of the grapes,' John Manduca told her. 'This starts during the grape harvest which takes place during the months of August and September and lasts for about five weeks.' Stopping in front of a sophisticated piece of machinery, he enlightened, 'This is a "stemmer" which bursts the grapes and separates the stems which are then discarded.' They walked on until they reached another huge machine. 'Following this process,' he continued, 'the "must" moves into a crusher which separates the skins and pips from the liquid "must". The grape juice is then pumped through tubing into fermentation tanks.' They entered a vault-like room containing massive steel tanks. Tara shivered slightly when cool air brushed her arms, yet was so absorbed she was barely conscious of discomfort. Hands reached out from behind her, rubbing warmth against her bare forearms. Instinctively she jerked from Falcon's reach just a split second before the manager broke off his conversation with Aithne to tell Tara, 'Fermentation usually lasts about three weeks. During this period the colour of the wine is obtained from the grape skins—for red wine the skins are left throughout the fermentation, but for rosé wine the skins are removed after a few days, when a pinkish colour is achieved.'

Somewhere along the line, between leaving the vault and progressing towards a plant—so noisy conversation was impossible—where bottles rattled along conveyor belts to be washed and sterilised, Tara became separated from the rest. She was loitering in front of an illuminated magnifying screen, exchanging smiles with girls whose job it was to make certain that no foreign bodies were present inside the bottles, when Falcon returned to her side. Miming that he wished to speak to her, he led her up a flight of stairs and into a room lined with steel sinks, rows and rows of bottles, their contents labelled with scientific names, and worktops holding bunsen burners, glass tubes and various other implements pertaining to laboratory work. He closed the door, and in contrast to the noise outside the room seemed eerily quiet, a vacuum of heavy silence. She slid a glance across his stern features, then turned aside, nervous of his mood, and prompted coldly:

'You think an apology sufficient to wipe out the memory of bestial behaviour?'

'I was referring to the misunderstanding that arose—not to the consequences of it, which,' he stressed hardly, 'could have been avoided by some-one less mutinously unco-operative or,' his tone softened, 'less foolishly loyal. Why didn't you tell me that it was Aithne who had taken the falcon?'

She started with surprise, then experienced the sweeping relief of being vindicated, without stopping to wonder why his good opinion should matter so much. 'How did you find out?' she whispered.

'As a director of the casino I have access to its books. It was not difficult to discover the real culprit. But you haven't answered my question—why did you allow me to believe that you were the guilty party?'

She swallowed hard, then decided there was no reason why he should not be told the truth. 'Aithne is young for her age, and given to impulsive actions. What she did was wrong, but she was carried along by the excitement of the moment and succumbed to temptation—something to which she is prone,' she said icily, 'as I hardly need to remind *you*. Besides that, she cares very much what you think of her.'

Seemingly unruffled by the implication that she did not, Falcon accepted her explanation. She knew he was smiling when, in a tone of amused indulgence, he stated, 'Aithne is a tantalising infant, swayed by impulse, as you say, but charming. We have become very close. I am surprised and a little disappointed that she did not come to me with her troubles.' He moved forward until he was standing by her side. She tensed, but kept her head bowed, watching lean brown hands playing idly with a tube of glass. She braced herself against the animal magnetism he projected, a powerful force that could reach her across the width of a room, sending blood rushing to her cheeks and a tingling awareness to her nerves. She felt overpowered, reminded against her will that in his arms she had known violent passion, that his virile body had imposed upon hers an intimacy greater than that allowed even to Bridget, who had fondled and bathed her as a child, a man with whom she had experienced a bonding of the flesh more personal than the tie existing between a mother and a child to whom she had given birth. His attraction to Aithne was proof, however, that he did not feel affected by any such bond.

'No doubt she would have,' she trembled, digging clenched fists into the pockets of her skirt, 'had she guessed you would feel such deep concern.'

The clinical atmosphere of the room became charged with meaningful silence. Tara could not look his way, but sensed that he was staring intently, weighing her words. Humiliation swamped her when, almost too casually, he asked, 'Are you jealous, Tara?'

She rounded so suddenly her elbow caught a glass phial, sending it crashing to the floor.

'Jealous?' Her eyes blazed green incredulity. 'Jealousy is a pain felt by a woman when she suspects that her love is not returned! How can you imagine me to be jealous when all I feel for you is hatred?'

Her words must have carried conviction, for he stepped back, his eyes bleak, a tight white line around his mouth.

'You wield your tongue like an eloquent whip, Tara, inflicting wounds that cut deep—too deep for the scars ever to heal.'

Aithne must have sensed the atmosphere between them as they drove away from the winery. Practically ignoring Tara, she put all her efforts into charming the smile back on to Falcon's lips and was rewarded when after a while he indicated what appeared to be a large house set in a hollow, its roof just visible from the road.

'Today, I think you deserve an extra special lunch. That house you see in the distance belongs to a friend of mine, Ben Vittoriosa. It was once a farmhouse, but the living was not so good, so a few years ago the family decided to turn it into a restaurant, cultivating only enough land to supply its needs. Ben is a superb chef; in a short space of time he has built up a reputation that is almost international.'

From outside the building looked nondescript. They entered through a doorway so low Falcon had to duck, then stepped straight into the medieval past. The interior was dim, the only lighting coming from candles stuck at intervals around the rim of a massive cartwheel suspended from the ceiling. Three of the walls were of undecorated stone, the fourth which accommodated a cavernous fireplace stretching the whole of its width, shone with brightly coloured tiles. Primitive farming implements studded every nook and corner, baskets and brasses were strewn over the walls and the large area of floor space was crammed with circular tables each having four high-backed wooden chairs placed around its perimeter.

A waiter moved forward to greet them, but as he was leading them towards a table a voice hailed them from the opposite side of the room.

'Falcon! Tara! Aithne! Come sit beside us, there's plenty of room!'

Obligingly the waiter veered towards the table from which Mario and Dolores were beckoning. The restaurant was not quite full, as yet, so they were able to choose a table near enough to allow a comfortable exchange of conversation.

Tara was pleased; there was a matter she wished to discuss with Dolores and she had been planning to get in touch with her. Aithne, however, looked sulky. So far as she was concerned the de Marcos had served their purpose, she no longer wished to associate with them.

Dolores beamed as she leant across to Tara. 'If you have not already done so, I suggest you try the *Lampuka*, our famous Maltese fish dish or, if you prefer, giant prawns, scampi or lobster. The chef de cuisine is certain to provide you with a unique and memorable meal.' The choice, however, was not to be left to them, for as they were trying to decide which dishes to sample the proprietor hastened to their table to greet them.

His first words underlined the depth of friendship existing between himself and Falcon. 'Oh, no, my friend!' He whisked the menus from out of their hands, 'Far too seldom do I have the pleasure of your company, and never before with a beautiful young bride. It shall be my great privilege to cook for you a very special meal, prepared by my own hands, and to offer it as a wedding gift to you both!'

As he bowed over Tara's hand she wished fervently that she had heeded Bridget's scolding. The rest of Ben Vittoriosa's clientèle was immaculately dressed, obviously considering a meal at his restaurant to be a special occasion. Her suspicion was confirmed when she glanced up and saw Falcon's expression of sardonic amusement. He had brought her here deliberately, as a punishment for her lack of interest in her appearance—clearly, he was gaining great satisfaction from her embarrassment.

Dolores and Mario had almost finished their meal so, during the interval that elapsed before the first course was served, Tara seized the opportunity to ask Dolores for her advice. Their chairs were back to back, making it easy for them both to put their heads together and chat almost inaudibly under the cover of general conversation being shared by Falcon, Aithne and Mario. She was all ears when in rapid undertone Tara appealed:

'I want your advice! Remember Falcon mentioning a party?' Dolores nodded. 'Well, he has insisted that I arrange it myself. The prospect is not so terrifying, it is merely that I would like it to be something special—a little out of the ordinary, if you know what I mean?'

'I know exactly what you mean,' Dolores smiled. 'This will be the first function presided over by the new Baroness and you naturally wish to surprise your husband and his friends by showing that you have a flair for entertaining.'

Actually, Falcon's request had been couched in such a deprecatory manner she had reacted to it as if to a challenge. 'Maria is an excellent cook,' he had told her, 'but she is becoming more and more easily flustered in her old age. Do what you can, but don't let the task worry you; everyone present will be prepared to make allowances for your youth and inexperience.'

'As a mark of my affection,' Dolores brought her back to earth, 'I will allow you to pinch an idea that has been simmering in my mind for some time. The Lebanese influence is quite strong throughout the island—how about a party with a Lebanese theme? There are dozens of traditional dishes from which to choose, numerous exciting cocktails, and as the highlight of the evening you could employ a belly dancer—they always go down well, especially with the men.'

The sparkle in Tara's eyes communicated enthusiasm. Dolores looked up and saw a waiter approaching, so she muttered quickly, 'I assume you want to keep the idea as a surprise. We must get together soon and iron out the details. Telephone me whenever it's convenient.'

Just then Ben appeared at the waiter's side and beamed, 'Now, my friends, I am ready to serve the best that I have to offer. I pray you will find it enjoyable!'

Enjoyable was not a word to do justice to a truly magnificent gastronomic experience. The meal began with marinated smoked salmon that had the consistency of oysters. A half lobster in a paprika, cream and white wine sauce followed and afterwards, to cleanse the palate, they were served a sorbet in grapefruit. Next came breast of duck and potato soufflé. Ben hovered all during the meal, his face wreathed in smiles, noting with appreciation the way in which they savoured each delicious mouthful, the delight they shared almost in silence because words of praise, however superlative, would have been inadequate. A classic Burgundy completed the entrée.

From a choice of fifty different cheeses Ben selected seven from the board, instructing Falcon, 'These, my friend, must be tasted in a clockwise direction, beginning with mild and progressing to strong.'

Falcon groaned, then reached for his glass to propose a toast. 'To Ben! No mere cook, but one upon whom the gods have bestowed the gift of transferring brilliance from the brain to the palate, from the palate to the fingertips!'

Ben responded with a sly chuckle. Flicking a look towards Tara, then back to Falcon, he teased, 'Eating is akin to making love—a seductive pleasure that ought to be enjoyed with abandon, or not at all!'

When both of the girls refused the cheese, Ben beckoned a waiter, then stood aside to make room for a trolley holding a dish containing a gigantic concoction of meringue, pastry and lemon. 'Try just a small piece!' he begged them.

'Oh, I couldn't!' Tara exclaimed, making a feeble gesture of protest.

Complacent in his assurance that she could not resist, he cocked an eyebrow in Falcon's direction. 'Like a girl with her lover for the first time,' he murmured, 'your wife protests: "Oh, no, what will you think of me!" Yet she knows she cannot refuse.'

Studiously Tara avoided her husband's eyes.

After such a repast there was really no alternative but to return home and rest. Even Aithne did not seem averse to the suggestion and looked almost relieved when Falcon nosed the car through the gateway of the M'Dina. Yet as Tara made her way upstairs she was surprised to find Aithne following her.

'I had intended to rest for an hour,' she told her pointedly when Aithne draped herself over the couch in the sitting room.

'And me,' she replied ungrammatically, smothering a yawn. 'But not until we've picked a bone together.'

'Picked a bone?' Tara repeated, weary of her sister's carping.

'Yes.' Aithne stared hard. 'Don't try to pretend you haven't attempted to ingratiate yourself into Falcon's good books by telling him it was I who took the trinket.'

'I didn't!' Tara began. 'He——'

'You must have,' Aithne cut in rudely. 'What other explanation could there be for his paying off my debt to the casino and presenting me with quite a sizeable cheque to cover expenses until Father's affairs have been resolved?'

Resentment flared through Tara's being, yet somehow she managed to retain a look of icy calm. 'You didn't accept, of course.'

Aithne looked amused. 'I most certainly did! "Take everything that he offers," Father said, and for the first time in my life I'm prepared to follow his advice.'

Tara dropped into a chair, her head bowed with the shame of feeling bitter contempt for her family. 'So Father has been begging from Falcon? He's told him everything ... ?'

'And laid self-pity on with a trowel, I shouldn't wonder,' Aithne nodded. 'Anyway, whatever he said was most effective.' She stood up and stretched like a satisfied cat. 'Falcon has taken complete control—he's told Father to leave everything in his hands.'

'Damn you!' Tara jumped to her feet, quivering uncontrollably. 'Damn you both for forcing me into such an invidious position! I told you I wanted to be under no obligation to him—all I want from Falcon is a divorce!'

Aithne's eyes narrowed as silkily she suggested, 'That might not be so hard to achieve as you've been led to think. Certain things Falcon has said during the past days have indicated to me that he may have had a change of mind—and heart. Why not broach the subject again?' she drawled, sauntering towards the door. 'I'm certain you'll find him eager to reverse his previous decision.'

CHAPTER ELEVEN

TARA lay back on her pillows staring at the ceiling. It was an incredible two months since the day of her wedding, eight weeks of tortured tension which had not lessened with the passage of time. Since the day of their visit to the winery Falcon had issued no further invitations to join in any of the outings he shared with Aithne. He had given up all pretence of wanting her company, which was hardly surprising considering the way Aithne hung upon his every word, flattering his battered ego with flirtatious looks and adoring smiles. Undoubtedly, she had been right about his change of heart. All that was required of Tara was that she should once more broach the subject of divorce—all signs indicated that this time her request would not be refused.

She planned to ask him tonight, once the party was over, the function she and Dolores had been organising for the past weeks, spending every spare moment with their heads together, deciding, rejecting, agreeing and sometimes disagreeing, right up until the last day when everything had miraculously fallen into place, leaving little left to do but wait for the few remaining hours to pass.

She stirred restlessly, stifling an urge to cry. Today should have been the happiest day of her life.

It was her twenty-first birthday, the day she was supposed to have taken over full control of her inheritance. The fact that there was nothing left to inherit hardly seemed to matter now—what was most hurtful was that there had been no mention of the imminent birthday. There was no way that Falcon could have known, of course, but neither Aithne nor her father had so much as hinted at the subject.

Hearing a rattle of the door handle, she eased herself up on the pillows, her face brightening. Bridget, of all people, would not have forgotten the importance of today.

'Good morning, alannah!' She bustled into the room with a tray of morning tea, poured out a cup, then handed it to Tara before crossing to the window to open the shutters. 'Another glorious day!' she exclaimed when sunshine spilled into the room. 'It may sound ungrateful, but I can't help missing the feel of soft Irish rain upon my face and the sight of sloping hills and lush green meadows. Eternal sunshine is all very well, but a surfeit of anything— even pleasure—soon palls.' She swung briskly towards the wardrobe. 'Now, which outfit do you intend wearing today? Something serviceable, no doubt, if you're to be kept busy with last-minute arrangements.'

Tara stared at Bridget's back with hurt-filled eyes. She, too, had forgotten! She gulped down a mouthful of tea that tasted horrible, then replaced the cup on the tray, threw back the bedcovers and swung her feet to the floor. Moping would not solve anything, neither would self-pity. Tomorrow she would probably be leaving the island—the only way to endure this last remaining day was to fill it with activity. She stood up. 'Slacks and a shirt will do, Bridget ...' then broke off with a gasp when the floor rose up to meet her, fell away, then lapsed into a nauseating rocking motion that became more pronounced when she sank back on to the bed.

Bridget's face wavered before her eyes as she reached out in panic and felt her hand caught in a cool grasp. 'There, there, my pet, you'll feel better in a minute,' Bridget soothed, holding her gently until the room stopped spinning.

'Bridget,' she trembled, 'what can be wrong? I've never before experienced such a peculiar sensation!'

'Of course you haven't,' Bridget agreed, puzzling Tara with a wide beaming smile, 'but don't worry, it's perfectly normal, in fact, I've been expecting something like this, all the signs pointed to it—lethargy, irritability, pallor, and now the most promising sign of all.'

'Sign of what?' Tara was beginning to wonder if Bridget had become affected by too much sun. It was unnatural for anyone to show such obvious delight at another person's discomfort. She became even more puzzled when Bridget laughed aloud and tightened her grip to administer an affectionate shake.

'You're such an innocent you haven't realised! Signs of pregnancy, my dear. You're going to have a baby!'

Sheer unadulterated shock drove Tara to her feet.

Taking a tight grasp on her reeling senses, she stormed:

'Don't be such an idiot, Bridget! Such a thing is simply not possible!'

Bridget, obviously bridling, threw a derogatory glance over the unused pillows on Tara's bed, then sniffed. 'You must be the best judge of that, but if you're not pregnant then my name isn't Bridget McBride!'

After she had stalked out Tara fell back on to the bed feeling stunned, cold, and terribly afraid. Tentatively, she began exploring her body with trembling hands, searching for physical signs, trying to draw comfort from the fact that her stomach was as flat, her waistline as trim, trying to convince herself that Bridget's wild surmise could not possibly have any basis in fact, that no tiny heart, no miniature replica of Falcon was gathering life and strength inside her body.

Her thoughts winged back to the first night they had spent together on Gozo, to the nuptial bower with its entwined hearts, embracing doves and symbols of fertility. Once again she felt the sensuous stroke of silken sheets against her skin, sniffed heady perfume that had drifted through the open window from the garden below, recalled the background symphony of sound caused by waves washing over rocks on the nearby shore, their turbulent heaving, their exultant hiss as urgent sea penetrated fissures in the cliff face, then the sigh as it retreated. All had been fitting accompaniments to the night when passion had erupted like a storm which, once fury had been spent, had left them huddled together exhausted, yet gloriously contented. Uttering a moan of agony, she twisted round to bury hot cheeks against pillows of cool lawn. *In the midst of that storm a child had been conceived!*

It was a long time before her rebellious body and mind relaxed and doubts and fears waned, giving way to numbed acceptance ...

It was well into morning when, looking outwardly calm and collected, she made her way downstairs. Breakfast had long since been cleared away, so she was surprised when she reached the foot of the stairs to discover Falcon prowling around the hall in a manner that could only be described as loitering. When he saw her he smiled, stampeding her pulses. She was looking at not just a man, her temporary husband, but at the father of her child! His eyes quizzed her almost frightened expression as he advanced to tower over her.

'I've been waiting for you,' he said, a little of his previous tenderness evident in his tone.

'Have you?' Her heart jumped to her throat. 'Why ... ?'

For a moment he did not reply, seeming content to let his glance rove faintly flushed cheeks, eyes full of hidden depths, and an unusually vulnerable mouth that would not be still. 'You look different,' he startled her by saying. 'Only yesterday it crossed my mind that you did not look well. I made a mental note to censure you for expending too much of your energy on this evening's party, and yet today there is a bloom about you ...' He paused when, panicked by the thought that he might have guessed her secret, she turned aside, then he continued in a brisk, matter-of-fact tone, 'There is something I want you to see. It won't take long,' he insisted when she seemed about to protest, 'ten minutes at the most.'

Tara felt pleased, as she slid into the front seat of the car, that some impulse had driven her into choosing a dress that suited her new mood of maturity, an appealingly feminine tunic of white broderie anglaise finely scalloped around the neck-line and hem, with wide sleeves gathered into tight wristbands. Belted around her narrow waist, the tunic fell pinafore fashion over a swirling skirt of emerald green. Falcon was reminded, as he glanced down at her, of a wide-eyed child waiting expect-antly for an outing.

She was too preoccupied to notice the direction he took as the car headed away from the M'Dina, but they had not been travelling for more than five minutes when he drew up at the side of the road, stepped out of the car, then helped her to alight. He strode a few paces, beckoning her to follow, then leant his elbows along the top of a gate guarding the entrance to a field. He inclined his head and curiously she followed the direction he had indi-cated. Two horses were grazing in the corner of the field, nuzzling parched grass in search of juicy blades. She stiffened, feeling a catch in her heart as she noted something familiar about a proudly-tossing main, an arrogant swish of tail ...

'Happy birthday, Tara,' Falcon murmured, throwing open the gate.

She cast him an incredulous look, then as realisation dawned sped past him, running the length of the field crying out loudly, 'Traleen! Caliph! Oh, you wonderful, beautiful darlings!'

With ears pricked, Traleen began ambling towards her, but was passed by Caliph's prancing hooves when, after a momentary hesitation, he began galloping towards his mistress. He emitted a great whinny of joy as she stumbled the last few yards and flung her arms around his neck. The first moments of meeting were chaotic as she fondled, kissed and cooed over the two friends to whom, in her heart, she had already said a last farewell.

She babbled in her excitement. 'Oh, Traleen, my love, you've lost weight! Were you seasick, did you hate your journey over the horribly bobbing sea? Whoa! Caliph, you mustn't get so excited. Steady, boy, steady!'

Then in the midst of it all, somewhere between a choke and a gulp, tears began to flow. This last traumatic incident coming on top of weeks of tension broke a proud spirit already badly bent. Her grief, silent at first, developed into shuddering sobs as she leant her head against Caliph, soaking the flank of the motionless animal who stood with tail drooping, ears flattened either side of his head, mystified by sounds that were spelling out louder than any words the misery and anguish of his young mistress.

Standing close behind, his eyes bleak, Falcon

waited until the flow had run dry then, placing a hand lightly on either side of her waist, he pulled her away.

'I had not realised the extent and depth of your unhappiness.' He addressed the back of her bowed head. Heavily, he concluded, 'Don't worry, Tara, you'll soon be home.'

His words penetrated her misery, causing her to wonder why the voicing of such a mundane fact should make him sound as if he were being torn apart.

She had thought the demented fates had finished with her for the day until, just an hour before the first guests were due to arrive at the Palazzo, she was summoned to the phone by a frantic Dolores. 'Tara,' she gasped, 'it's the belly dancer! You know we arranged to give her a lift because she had no transport? Well, she slipped getting into the car and has sprained her ankle. It is so badly swollen that there is no possible chance of her being able to dance tonight!'

'Oh, no!' Tara breathed. 'Can we get a replacement, do you think?'

'No chance.' Dolores' tone was emphatic. 'What few dancers there are on the island are booked up weeks ahead. It is no simple art, but takes months of training.' She paused, her attention caught by a quickly-indrawn breath.

'Would you ask her if she would mind lending me her outfit?' Tara urged. 'Just for this evening.'

'No, of course not,' Dolores sounded puzzled,

'I'm sure she'll have no objection. But why ...?'

'Just bring it with you,' Tara insisted. 'I must finish dressing. I'll explain everything when you arrive.' Thoughtfully, she dropped the telephone receiver into its cradle. An idea had come to her on the spur of the moment and the more she thought about it the more appealing it became. The success of this evening's party had grown more and more important until now it was paramount in her mind. She was determined that nothing was going to spoil it because it was to be her swan song—tonight, when she asked Falcon for a divorce, she was certain he would agree. That being so, she intended wasting no time in leaving the island, she would take the first available flight home; Falcon's far-reaching influence would no doubt ensure that a seat would be made available for her tomorrow. But before she went she wanted to leave him with a reminder. He had many faults, but meanness was not one of them—ensuring the success of tonight's party was the only way she knew of expressing her gratitude, a small thank-you for the tolerance he had shown towards her family and most of all for uniting her once more with her animal friends.

She had just finished dressing when Falcon appeared to escort her downstairs. He strolled into her bedroom with his usual air of having a perfect right to be there. A white dinner jacket sat easily upon broad shoulders, a dark wine-coloured shirt with frilled jabot and cuffs was a perfect match for finely-creased slacks tailored to fit immaculately over lean hips and muscular thighs. A diamond stud glistened in his cuff as he reached out to hold her at arm's length while slowly he took stock of her appearance.

She withstood his scrutiny without fear. When the mood took her she could achieve outstanding glamour. This evening she had taken special pains, choosing for this important occasion a 'big' dress made up of many yards of exotic fabric printed with a floral design picked out in turquoise, mauve and just a hint of green on a background of frozen blue. A deeply scooped neckline left her shoulders bare; very full sleeves, crisply puffed, fell below a gathering band pushed up above each elbow, and beneath the widely tented skirt peeped a frilled petticoat in a deeper shade of turquoise. It was a dress that needed rehearsal and for a long time she had practised sitting and standing to ascertain how it moved, to decide whether it looked best loose or belted, choosing the exact shade of tights and shoes so that once her ensemble had been decided she was able to relax, confident that she was looking her best.

The result of her efforts was reflected in Falcon's admiring eyes. 'You are a beautiful enigma,' he murmured, his glance that of a hungry man confronted by a banquet he had been forbidden to touch, 'one day *gamine*, the next an enticing romantic.' He brooded down, tracing with one finger the silken sweep of fiery chignon, then veered, tempted by the childish contrast of soft wisps teasing cheeks and brow. He seemed to hold himself in check as regretfully he murmured, 'How I wish there was time to show you our blue grotto! It can only be reached by boat, a cavern that the sea gouged out of the cliffs and then used as a miser's treasure house, filling it with every jewelled shade of sea. It is said that it is a favourite meeting place of sirens who hold sea-farers spellbound with their midnight song. Though it is named "blue", only there have I seen a shade of green that bears comparison with your lovely eyes.'

Tara had to remind herself that guests were arriving, that downstairs servants awaited her instructions, that the success of the evening depended upon her ability to keep a cool head. 'We'd better go downstairs,' she stammered, inching out of reach of his tenseness, steeling herself against the unexpected pain of caring that her cool rebuff had resulted in a sudden tightening of his jaw.

He winced, then squared his shoulders and politely agreed, 'Of course, we must be present when our guests arrive.'

For days the huge ballroom had been put out of bounds to everyone but the servants, Tara and Dolores, who had helped design the decor, the lighting, the arabesque patterns that combined to make a sophisticated setting in true Lebanese style. As guests entered, musicians began to play music attuned to the magical atmosphere; hired waiters circulated with trays of drinks containing cocktails made from the secret recipes of Omar Khayyam: *Xarba Al-Hana*—a temptation of arak and rum with a hint of lemon, topped up with champagne; and *Merhba*—a festive delight of dry gin added to crême de Cassis and decorated with a sprig of mint.

'*Al-Hana!*' Falcon lifted his glass in a wry toast.

'A Lebanese word meaning contentment. He who knows contentment is rich—behold, a pauper!' Savagely he tossed his head and downed the drink in one gulp.

Uneasily, once the last of the guests had been greeted, Tara edged away from his side, alarmed by his mood of brooding bitterness, by a voice which, since her last rebuff, had developed a cutting edge.

Congratulations floated in the air. As she circulated amongst the guests she was complimented on all sides by people enthralled by the unusual atmosphere, taking full advantage of tempting delicacies created by their most valuable find—a chef immigrant from Beirut whose specialities were *homus* —stuffed vine leaves; flaming kebabs, and *fatayer*— savoury pastries filled with spinach, onions and lemon.

Because of an agitated fluttering in her stomach, she found that she was quite incapable of sampling any of the dishes, but was forcing herself to nibble at a sweetmeat when she felt a touch on her arm and swung round to see Dolores, beaming and shiny-eyed.

'Isn't it terrific? They all came here tonight prepared to endure yet another boring, formal dinner, and they are now babbling with delighted surprise! The party is a real swinger, so much so that the lack of a belly dancer is of no consequence.'

'You brought her outfit?'

'Yes,' Dolores nodded, 'I handed it to Bridget who has taken it up to your room. But I still don't understand——'

'You will,' Tara promised with a secretive smile, then shook her head when Dolores prepared to launch further questions. 'You must be patient,' she insisted, 'or the surprise will be spoilt.'

With a small moue of disappointment, Dolores swept a glance around the couples on the dance floor, her eyes narrowing as they alighted upon Aithne clinging closer to Falcon than was strictly necessary as they moved in unison. She was no fool, she had long since recognised Aithne's reluctance to continue their friendship, but there was no malice in her voice, only concern for Tara, when dryly she observed, 'With a husband as handsome as yours, I would be reluctant to allow any woman too much licence—even a sister.'

Following the direction of her eyes, Tara stiffened, resenting this censure. 'Aithne is still very immature, but the same can't be said of Falcon. If her head is being turned then the blame must be his, because, after all,' she reminded Dolores with asperity, 'they were very close friends before I arrived on the island.'

Dolores's eyebrows rose so high they almost disappeared. 'You surprise me!'

It was Tara's turn to stare. 'How is that possible? You, of all people, must be aware of their former attachment—you introduced them, Aithne was living under your roof when their friendship developed into an affair!'

'Aithne? And Falcon?' Dolores exclaimed, then with a quick glance around lowered her voice to an undertone. 'My dear Tara, until he met you Falcon was extremely careful never to commit himself to any woman. As any of the scheming mammas present here tonight could tell you, he has always kept himself aloof—not at all averse to enjoying female company, yet managing with chivalrous politeness to withdraw his attentions from any girl foolish enough to show signs of wanting a deeper involvement. It became almost a game between the islanders, speculating upon the stage a friendship had reached and, if the girl's infatuation became too obvious, how long it would be before he excused himself and disappeared for weeks to his home on Gozo, the retreat which no one but yourself has ever been allowed to share.'

Tara felt the colour draining from her cheeks. She drew in a deep, steadying breath. 'That may have been the way the situation looked to outsiders,' she argued, 'but how could anyone presume to know for certain how deeply he was involved? In Aithne's case—'

'Aithne's case,' Dolores interrupted firmly, 'was one of complete non-involvement. Not for want of trying on her part, I hasten to add, but because of lack of interest on Falcon's. As you pointed out earlier, I was there, I saw what happened—or rather, what did not happen. All during her stay she wangled invitations to parties where she was most likely to bump into him, she tried in every way she could think of to attract his attention—in fact, her infatuation became so blatantly obvious that hostesses became wary of issuing further invitations in order to save him embarrassment. But they needn't have bothered, for he was completely unaware of her existence. At the time, his mind was centred solely upon a young American girl who was newly arrived on the island.' She chuckled. 'I think the secret of his success with our sex is the way he becomes entirely absorbed in any woman whom he finds interesting. He is, without a doubt, an all or nothing man.' She tapped Tara playfully on the cheek. 'Consider yourself fortunate, my dear; Falcon is a notoriously wily bird, yet he did not hesitate to forsake freedom in favour of marriage to you!'

Tara drew away, unable, unwilling to believe that Aithne could have lied. 'As you say,' she agreed shakily, 'he is wily—and clever,' she murmured under her breath, 'clever enough to realise that a reputation for integrity can be maintained by ensuring that one's indiscretions are never found out.'

The subject of their conversation suddenly appeared at her side. 'Shall we dance?' he invited gravely, leading her on to the floor before she had time to frame an excuse.

If he was sharing her torture he did not show it as he held her close, moving in time with music, modern in tempo, yet as sensuous as that which centuries ago conquering corsairs had employed as an ally to sublimate fear and to weaken the resistance of their female captives. Tara chanced a look at an aquiline profile that might have belonged to one of the invading Arabs who had seized the capital, renamed it M'dina, then, showing the pos-

sessive streak ingrained within the sons of Adam,
built around it a protective wall and dug a deep,
deterring moat.

'Relax,' he murmured, pulling her closer, 'your
party is wonderfully successful. I am proud of
you!' The tenderly spoken compliment was almost
her undoing. She jerked a space between them,
feeling his nearness an intolerable strain on her
nerves, his touch a torch setting light to dormant
emotions.

As soon as the music stopped she slipped out of
his arms and fled upstairs to her room. It was almost
time for the finale, the highlight of the evening.

Less than a year ago she had seen advertised a
course of lessons in belly dancing for beginners. She
and her friends had hooted with laughter at the
thought, then, motivated by an impulse to surprise
her circle of rather blasé young friends, she had en-
rolled for the course, surprising herself and her
teacher by proving to be a natural in the art of the
undulating navel.

She stepped out of her dress, then, gasping with
shock at the scantiness of the costume, she wriggled
her way into a jewelled bra designed to uplift the
breasts so that they were rounded as pomegranates,
leaving a deep cleavage exposed. The skirt was no
more than a jewelled band with wisps of chiffon
attached which nestled low upon the hips, well
below the navel. Without daring to look in a mirror,
she unpinned her hair, then brushed it until it fell,
a red flag of courage, past creamy shoulders.

The music stopped as she ran down the stairs and

hesitated outside the door leading into the ballroom. The floor had cleared of dancers and the bandleader, obviously on the look-out, caught sight of her, and upon receipt of a prearranged signal swung round facing the band, raising his hand to lead them into the mystical, erotic music of the East.

Tara's mind went blank the moment she sidled into the circle left by the dancers. Slowly she began pivoting her hips, keeping time with the tempo of the music. With growing enthusiasm she went into her full repertoire of hip bumps, belly rolls, hip circles, stomach flutters, shoulder shakes, pelvic thrusts and, for good measure, the buttock bump—combining the stomach flutter with the hip circle for a double exciting effect. She was delighted to discover that she could still manage to do the belly roll—the most difficult movement of all and one absolutely essential to the dance, which entailed holding her breath and panting with her stomach muscles so that her abdomen moved quickly in and out, an exercise that looked abandoned and devastatingly sensuous.

She was breathless with exertion when the music reached its final crescendo and she dropped to her knees on the floor, her head bowed between outstretched arms, awaiting the expected applause.

All she heard was a thunderous clap of silence.

Bewildered, she raised her head just in time to see Falcon striding towards her, his expression thunderous. Like a piece of thistledown she was plucked from the floor and carried none too gently through a crowd of guests whose shocked, stunned faces she just managed to glimpse as she was whisked past. He spoke not a word until he had dumped her in the middle of her room and re-traced his steps to kick shut the door.

She shrank from eyes glittering with intense fury, sensing that he was angrier than she had ever seen him, yet utterly bewildered as to the cause. He wasted no time putting his rage into hard, bitter words.

Raking her trembling form exposed by the tawdry costume, he bit out, 'Enough is enough! From the day of our marriage you have gone out of your way to demonstrate lack of respect for my feel-ings, contempt of my beliefs, dislike of my friends and a deep hatred of myself. Yet knowing all that, I did not suspect that you would stoop to the depths of degradation by exposing your almost naked body to the stares of my friends, flaunting and gyrating in the manner of an Arabian *houriyeh*, in order to shame me!'

She gasped, beginning dimly to realise the extent of her sin. She knew that Falcon held liberal views on most subjects and had considered him so modern-minded it had not occurred to her that, so far as his wife was concerned, he might adhere to a strict moral code excluding even a hint of feminine daring. Yet even so, he was over-reacting. This was the twentieth century, yet incredibly, he was displaying the attitude of one influenced by Arab forebears whose wives had been executed for so much as un-covering their faces!

He began speaking again, his words penetrating

her shocked mind. She had to concentrate hard, and felt a surge of dismay when more quietly, he rebuffed, 'The irony of it is, Tara, that you had already made your point. This morning, when I realised how unhappy you were, I forced myself to face the fact that the prospect of any future happiness was bleak—that there could be no future for us together.' He turned aside so that all she saw of his face was a tense line of jaw when, sounding unutterably weary, he conceded, 'You've won, Tara. You may have your divorce.'

CHAPTER TWELVE

FALCON'S voice seemed to come from very far away. For long, silent minutes Tara simply stood and stared at the man who had just promised her her freedom, his words hammering like a battering ram upon the door of her mind behind which lay knowledge secreted even from herself. The barrier gave way with a shock that reverberated through her entire body, forcing her—too late—to face the fact that she did not want a divorce. That she was deeply and insanely in love with him!

Words of protest rose to her lips and were bitten back. He must never know of her regret, never guess that the thought of walking out of his life, of never again seeing his face or thrilling to his touch, was such agony it forced from her a gasp which must have sounded to him like relief.

His face darkened. 'Get changed,' he ordered curtly, striding towards the door leading into the sitting-room, 'I'll wait for you in here.'

'I can't go back downstairs!' she gasped, horrified at the idea of facing curious eyes that might read the secret she felt sure was emblazoned on her face.

He turned from the door to insist gently, 'You must, if only for Bridget's sake. She, too, has been planning a surprise. At this very moment she is downstairs waiting to light the candles on the birth-day she has been slaving over for days. You must not disappoint her. You have great courage, Tara,' he concluded softly, 'do not allow it to fail you now.'

It was as hard as she had imagined it would be to return downstairs, trying to look nonchalant as she mingled with guests who stared, then averted embarrassed eyes. But Falcon's presence close by her side provided her with the strength to laugh and chat as if nothing untoward had happened, her courage immensely bolstered when Falcon—usually very reserved in public—demonstrated affection by keeping an arm around her shoulders and smiling with fond solicitude into her eyes. Once, when he sensed her wilting, he even bent so far as to brush his lips across her flushed cheek.

Gradually, the faces of their guests relaxed into smiles. Knowing nudges were exchanged as they read into his attitude exactly the impression he wished to convey—that there had been a lovers' tiff, but that the Baroness, in the manner of all new brides, had exerted her wiles to appease her hus-band's possessive jealousy.

Even Aithne was deceived. Seizing upon a moment when Falcon's attention was temporarily diverted, she cornered Tara to demand, 'What's going on? I've never known Falcon so demonstra-tive!'

For the first time in her life Tara experienced a fierce stab of jealousy and recognised it as such. However genuine Aithne's claims, Falcon was still her husband and just for these last two hours she felt justified in pretending a permanency in their relationship.

Unable to trust herself to give an intelligible answer, she side-stepped Aithne's furious stare and sidled back to his side. Immediately his arm closed protectively around her shoulders. He glanced down at her face, his eyes pinpointing as, urged on by reckless despair, she sent him a radiant smile.

Without change of expression she withstood the pain of his punishing grip and felt a sense of deprivation when, as her father's voice boomed close, he released her arm and moved away.

'How is my birthday girl?' As O'Toole repeated his fatuous question Tara could barely suppress a surge of dislike of the man who had intruded upon a rare moment. Resentment flashed in her eyes as, in a low undertone, she rebuked, 'I suggest you go easy on the drink, Father. It seems to me that you've already had more than enough.'

'Blame yourself, my dear,' he grinned, not one bit deflated, 'and Omar Khayyam, of course. I'm not the only one who's finding it hard to resist such delicious champagne cocktails. And why should I even try? After all, it isn't every day that a man gets to celebrate his daughter's coming-of-age. I missed out on the wedding celebrations but, by jove, I intend to enjoy this party! Yes, darling child, every time my glass is filled I'll offer a toast to your wisdom, for if you hadn't had the good sense to marry the Baron we'd now be known as the homeless and penniless O'Tooles!'

Feeling a mixture of anger and embarrassment,

Tara edged him towards a window that opened on to a terrace. Glancing round to ensure they could not be overheard, she shattered his complacency: 'I don't have time to elaborate upon the contempt I feel for the way in which you went begging to Falcon, but this much I can tell you. Falcon has agreed to a divorce, so tomorrow I'm returning to Ireland. If you have any sense of decency at all, you'll come with me. For a while we can stay with Aunt Peg, I'm sure she won't mind putting us up until we sort out the mess we're in and find somewhere else to live.'

O'Toole looked stupefied. 'Holy Mother! Are you mad? You must know that Falcon has taken over my commitments, so why should we stay with your aunt when our home is ready and waiting? And what's all this nonsense you speak about divorce? Your husband loves you, and don't try to tell me that you don't feel the same way about him —knowing women as well as I do, I wouldn't hesitate to call you a liar.'

She had no wish to argue that point, but her voice was firm when she insisted, 'I will not touch a penny of Falcon's money. We may be poor, but we're still capable of work—we could start up a riding stable, Father,' she encouraged eagerly, 'you know all there is to know about horseflesh and I'm an expert rider. All our friends would rally round, I'm sure we would make a go of it!'

As her father glared apoplectic rage, Aithne ran on to the terrace. 'Tara,' she beckoned, 'Bridget is bringing in your cake.' Throwing a last pleading look in her father's direction, Tara stepped inside the ballroom and immediately the lights were dimmed so that attention was focused upon the cake being wheeled into centre of the room on a trolley pushed by a beaming Bridget.

As the band struck up 'Happy Birthday', Falcon took her hand and led her through an applauding throng that was enthusiastically singing the birthday anthem. Across the width of twenty-one flickering candles their eyes met.

'Make a wish!' he urged, projecting a smile of loving tenderness for the benefit of their audience.

She drew in a deep, quivering breath and blew hard until every candle was extinguished, leaving a residue of blue smoke curling from each tiny wick, charred as her emotions, exuding a pungent, throat-catching reminder of children's voices, massed flowers, grave intonations, and the solemn face of the man to whom she had addressed the words: '*With my body I thee worship,*' unaware, as she had spoken, that that vow she had made was truthful.

She blinked tears from eyes full of regret for a wish she knew could never be fulfilled and managed somehow to communicate her appreciation. She cut the first slice of cake, then left Bridget to supervise the distribution of the rest amongst guests whose smiles showed that they had forgiven the young Baroness her earlier *faux pas*, excusing her on the grounds of her youth and the innocence of her ways.

The smile seemed cemented upon her lips, her conversation that of an automaton issuing programmed responses when, knowing she could not endure another moment, she appealed to Falcon, 'Do you think I might be excused? The day has been rather a strain.'

'Of course,' he was quick to respond, 'some of the guests are about to leave, anyway.' He escorted her to the foot of the stairs and was about to rejoin their guests when she uttered his name.

'Falcon!'

'Yes?' As he spun round light from a chandelier fell upon his face. With a pang, Tara noted signs of strain around his mouth, weariness lurking in the depths of his eyes.

'I should like to leave tomorrow, if possible.'

'So soon?' His tone was flat, his face expressionless. He shrugged. 'Very well, it shall be arranged.'

Tara was lying prone, still fully dressed, on top of her bed when Bridget walked into her bedroom half an hour later. 'What's all this?' She bustled forward. 'You ought to be in bed, my dear, you must take care not to become overtired.'

She was shocked at the whiteness of the face Tara turned towards her. 'I know it's late, Bridget, but would you mind helping me to pack? We shall be returning home tomorrow.'

'Home?' Bridget bristled. 'And where might that be, pray?'

'Please don't be difficult, Bridget,' Tara's voice broke, 'you know very well what I mean. We're returning to Ireland. The Baron has agreed to a divorce; the sooner I get out of his life the better for us both.'

Speechless with shock, Bridget collapsed on to the bed beside her. 'I don't understand ...' Her lined face seemed to have aged in seconds. 'You can't wipe out a marriage as easily as that!'

'Our marriage was a mistake, an error for which I accept entire responsibility,' Tara replied, quietly breaking her heart. 'I ought never to have interfered. It's Aithne he loves—Aithne whom he's always loved.'

'Rubbish!' Bridget found her voice. Rigid with indignation, she declared, 'I don't believe a word of it—nor did I, from the very beginning! I know that young spalpeen too well, I've watched her carefully, noting how she tries to flatter him with words, to keep his eyes from straying in your direction—which they always do whenever he thinks you're not watching. For some reason known only to himself, he has tolerated Aithne's silly ways without a murmur of annoyance, but of one thing I'm certain—it is you that he loves.'

With a flash of hauteur, Tara taunted, 'Would you have me believe my sister is a liar?'

'Would you try to maintain that she is entirely without fault?' Bridget asked sadly. 'No one is perfect, child. Have I loved you any the less because you're stubborn and wilful? Though I hate to admit it, Aithne has always shown signs of a jealous nature. As a child she coveted your dolls; as a teenager she resented your popularity, and as you grew older and more beautiful she became incensed by the ease with which you were able to attract every man in your vicinity. The fact that your grandmother made you her sole beneficiary didn't help matters. I'm afraid, Tara, my love, you must come to terms with the fact that initially Aithne's lies may have been mere exaggerations of the truth, but now she has reached the stage where she'll stop at nothing in order to wreck your happiness.'

'No!' Tara choked out the denial. 'I refuse to believe her capable of such a thing! She's my *sister*!'

'And Cain and Abel were brothers,' Bridget snapped, her face grim.

Tara felt torn in two, appalled by Bridget's reasoning on the one hand, and on the other, deeply ashamed of *wanting* her words to be true. That Aithne could have been so cruel ... ! That Falcon should have been so punished ... !

'*Bridget!*' Tara collapsed into the old woman's arms and began to sob, abandoning herself to the storm of misery so long dammed up inside of her. For a long time Bridget held her close, petting and murmuring in an attempt to soothe away remorse from a tense body suffering on the rack of retribution. Rapidly she talked, urging, pleading, using any words she thought might help to convince Tara that she would be wrong to leave her husband or his island home.

'You must go to the Baron and explain, tell him that you've changed your mind, be humble, if necessary, ask his pardon, but for heaven's sake don't deprive him of his rights, the joy of knowing he's to be a father, the pleasure of watching his child grow up. Maltese people set great store by customs, especially one ancient one that is connected with a child's first birthday,' Bridget told her softly, heartened by the fact that Tara had stopped sobbing and was now lying quietly listening, 'it's known as *Il Quċċija*. Relatives assemble and the child is brought into the room. If it be a boy, he is presented with two baskets, coins, an inkstand, a sword, and other manly articles. The choice he makes on this occasion is taken as an indication of his future disposition and the mode of life he will embrace. Should he choose the coin, it is taken as a sign of a liberal character; if he prefers the inkstand he is thought to favour either trade or the Bar; if he takes up the sword the greatest hopes are entertained of his courage. Naturally, if the child is a girl, needles, silks and ribbons are supplied in place of the sword and the inkstand.'

With eyes half closed Tara rested her head against Bridget's shoulder, so exhausted by turbulent emotion she had not the strength to disperse from her mind the image Bridget's insidious voice had conjured. Falcon's small, black-haired son would naturally choose the sword. Cast in his father's image, endowed with blood from a mixture of proud, brave, intrepid ancestors, he would be taught by his father to use his talents well, to be courageous, to be strong yet kind to others weaker than himself, to be possessive and yet at the same time indescribably tender.

When she heard a sound that was half moan, half sigh, Bridget shook her. 'You must tell him!

Once he knows about the baby he'll never allow you to leave.'

'*No!*' Tara tore out of her arms to quiver the accusation. 'That would be tantamount to blackmail. He must *never* know!'

Such stubbornness was more than Bridget's Irish temper could stand. Casting discretion to the winds, she harangued with all the fury of a mother forced to stand helpless, watching her child rush into an act of self-destruction.

'I'm disgusted with you, Tara! For weeks now I have watched you moping in the manner of a spineless creature with neither gumption nor intelligence, letting your sister trample all over you, allowing your father to bully and bluster, accepting every degrading incident without showing a spark of fight! Where is the Tara I once knew? The one with her grandmother Rooney's fire in her veins, the one who never in her life hesitated to accept a challenge or who, whenever she was attacked, retaliated with all the spunk of a Kilkenny cat! You say the Baron loves Aithne? Very well, make him prove it. You attracted him once without even trying—if he means anything at all to you, you can do so again. He is your husband, the father of your child. My advice to you is this, alannah—if you want him, get out there and fight for him!'

Weary of Bridget's persistent nagging, Tara dismissed her, undressed, and slipped into bed. She was tired, yet for an hour she tossed and turned, her mind in too much of a turmoil to allow her to sleep. It was long past midnight when she threw back the covers and walked across to the window to open the shutters.

It was a soft, balmy night full of indigo shadows, yet it was still light enough to be able to discern the outlines of buildings surrounding the courtyard and the fountain tinkling in its centre. It was hard to accept that this was to be her last evening in Malta, that never again would she enjoy the beauty of small, deeply-incurving bays, of swimming in water clear as glass and deep sapphire blue, of seeing rows of pumpkins left to mellow on farmhouse roofs, or to wander through luxuriant gardens with lily ponds sheltering shoals of exotic fish, where lizards basked in the heat of sun-bathed paths and darted between the feet of strolling sightseers. Tara wished she had taken more photographs of towering cliffs, of golden-coloured stone, of the multi-coloured boats crammed into tiny harbours, of the palaces, the churches and the cathedrals that were so much a part of Falcon's island.

She wondered what he would think of Ireland, of its rolling green hills, rivers surging with trout, and the quiet solitude of countryside through which one could gallop for miles without encountering another living soul.

She jerked, reminded that Caliph and Traleen would have to be left behind until they could be transported back to Ireland. The poor creatures would be bewildered by her absence. However rushed tomorrow might be, she must find time to visit them before she left, to whisper reassurance and to promise that their parting would not be prolonged.

Spurred by impulse, she ran across to the wardrobe and threw open the doors, searching for slacks and a jumper. She would go now! The field where they were grazing was no more than ten minutes' walking distance from the M'Dina.

Minutes later she was tramping the empty roads with the gateway of the Silent City looming darkly behind her. Soft air brushed her cheeks, and as she walked she felt tension easing as the peace and solitude of the night helped her to relax for the first time in days.

Her footsteps quickened when she rounded a corner and recognised the path that led towards the field. As she neared the gate she was surprised to hear a soft whinny and wondered if there existed some sort of animal telepathy that had warned Caliph and Traleen of her approach. She saw the outline of a horse's head stretching across the top rail of the gate, then stopped dead when a tall shadow moved and spoke her name.

'Tara? What brings you here so late at night?'

Falcon had been leaning with his elbows on the gate talking to Caliph. His black hair was tousled, as if after pulling a sweater over his head he had been too impatient to look for a comb.

'I couldn't sleep,' she jerked, cursing the impulse that had led her into this trap.

But he seemed almost disinterested as he resumed his previous stance. 'Nor could I,' he replied laconically, stroking the muzzle of the horse who was nudging his shoulder with affection.

Surprised, and a little resentful, she stepped forward. 'I've never known Caliph do that to a stranger.'

For an instant she saw teeth flashing white in the darkness. 'Perhaps he senses an affinity between us?' he suggested.

She did not reply. The only common denominator between him and Caliph was herself—it might be dangerous to probe.

When Traleen ambled up to the gate Tara reached out to stroke her, heartened by the old mare's loyalty. 'You will miss them both when you return,' Falcon stated, his tone flat. 'I'll have them shipped back to you as soon as possible.'

'Thank you ...' she gulped, then, feeling the solitary word inadequate, she stumbled on. 'Thank you for everything, for your generosity and kindness to myself and to my family.' She drew herself up and continued with quiet dignity, 'I don't know to what extent we are in your debt, but when I get home I shall look for a job. It may take a long time, but I hope eventually to repay our debt in full.'

'Don't speak to me of debts and repayment, Tara!' His tone was sharp. 'You owe me nothing—on the contrary, it is I who owe you an apology. Nothing I have done can completely atone for my transgressions, but I shall be grateful if you will accept what small amount of financial aid I have given without argument. Consider it, if you will, an act of expiation for my sins.'

'Sins ... ?' she quavered.

Without turning his head, he nodded. 'Yes, I'm afraid they have been many. Haste was my undoing —over-eagerness my greatest error. Why,' he mused, speaking as if to himself, 'does one assume that because one loves one must be loved in return?' He sighed, then turned towards her. 'I rushed you through courtship which, in its strictest sense, is the period set aside before marriage for a couple to get to know each other. I imposed sexual maturity upon an innocent.' When she gasped a protest, he insisted, 'Yes, Tara, I know that yesterday you received the symbolic key that unlocks the door between adolescence and adulthood, but you have not yet, either spiritually or mentally, stepped across that threshold. Perhaps society is at fault for leading us to expect that a girl will adapt to an adult role immediately she is given to a man in marriage.'

'You make me sound very inadequate,' she choked, her cheeks burning.

'Inadequate?' He considered. 'No, that was certainly not my intention. Immature, perhaps, immune from the lightning flash that lit the spark of love in me—but not in you.'

'What is your definition of love, Falcon? Do you consider sexual attraction a sufficient basis for marriage?'

For the first time they were groping their way towards understanding without the distraction of physical contact. In their hasty courtship, their stormy marriage, there had been no time to probe the depths of each other's minds with easy conversation.

'Love is need,' he told her simply. 'But unless two people can thrill to each other's touch, voice and look, unless all of their senses are alive to each other, they are not in love.'

Tara felt isolated, completely cut off from him when he spoke with such finality. After much soul-searching, he seemed to have accepted the fact that he must cut her out of his life. She shivered, as if at the touch of ice-cold fingers, but whereas once such an action would have drawn him immediately to her side, he remained aloof, though he voiced concern.

'There is a wind rising. I'll take you back to the Palazzo.'

As they strolled back with a yard of space between them, he surprised her with the remark, 'I often find myself comparing you with my mother—there are marked similarities—a coolness of manner, for instance; a love of animals; a deep appreciation of beauty, a courageous spirit.'

'You loved her very much?' she asked softly.

'What little I knew of her. Physically she was present, but her mind and heart were buried with my father beneath the waves.'

'I'm sorry,' she stammered, feeling once again an ache of pity for the lonely boy he must have been.

'Don't be. She taught me how to cope with loneliness. I feel her loss still, but not so much as I felt the lack of a father in my earlier years. A boy needs a father to teach him *machismo*, the cult of manhood, how to act in a manner that is honourable and dignified. It is terribly difficult for a boy to acquire without a father's example the subtle knowledge of what it means to be a man.'

His words were still reverberating in her mind when they parted outside her door. Standing a pace away, he wished her a grave: 'Goodnight, Tara.' It sounded like goodbye.

She spun away, incapable of making a reply, her throat choked with tears as she watched his tall figure looking erect, proud, yet somehow lonely as he strode towards his room.

Machismo! The word he had used pounded her brain as she paced her bedroom floor. The belief that a man has to behave in a certain fashion in order to be a man was not new to her, but the importance it played in the lives of men in whose veins ran the blood of Spanish *conquistadores* had only now been brought home to her. Her son would inherit such blood!

Deep in thought, she undressed, slipped into a nightdress, then with her palms pressed flat against her body, she prayed for guidance. There was now no doubt in her mind that beneath her hands, deep inside her body, flickered a small flame of life. She was equally sure that her child would be a boy— Falcon's son. Did she have the right to deprive him of his inheritance, the *machismo* that Falcon had insisted was so important to a boy? She thought of the alternative and shuddered. Brought up in Ireland he would have only O'Toole's example to follow: an example of selfishness, over-indulgence, and a total absence of regard for his family. The choice, so far as her child was concerned, was self-evident. But what of herself? *If you want him*, Bridget had said. She did want him. Her love for him was all-consuming!

She sped across the room, her bare feet making no sound on the carpeted floor, and before her courage could desert her, turned the knob of the door connecting their two rooms, silently pushing it ajar. Falcon had not bothered to undress but lay fully clothed on top of his bed, staring up at the ceiling. Tara bit back a gasp of pity as she noted a furrowed brow, a profile etched with tension, the slight twitch of a muscle at the corner of his mouth. As she watched, his fingers flexed, showing physical frustration as he wrestled with his troubled thoughts.

Light from the bedroom beyond threw her slim body into sharp relief as she stood nymph-like in a diaphanous nightdress, waiting to be noticed.

'Falcon ...' she whispered.

Though the sound was barely audible his head snapped towards her. He blinked at the vision that might have materialised out of his dreams, then taut as wire he raised himself on one elbow and enquired in a cool distant manner:

'What is wrong, Tara? Is there something you want?'

'*Falcon!*' Hearing his name uttered on a broken sob sent him bounding to his feet. He hesitated, mere inches away from her, still unsure, his sombre eyes probing her face, enquiring—*demanding* guidance. His jaw muscles were tight, his mouth a stern straight line when, holding himself firmly in check, he insisted:

'Tell me what it is that you you want, Tara!'

'I want you!' she sobbed, her proud spirit humbled. 'Oh, Falcon, I love you so much!'

She stumbled forward into arms opened wide to receive her, sobbing her misery, heartache and regret against his chest as he held her close, murmuring matching phrases of contrition, apology and fierce condemnation of himself, until they had both expiated their grief.

Thankfulness was the overriding emotion they shared as they clung together as one, dazed by the magnanimity of fate that had torn down barriers erected by pride, misunderstanding, and the interference of others. It was a long time before Falcon could bear to prise himself far enough away to cup her face in his hands and to demand hoarsely:

'My darling, never again do I want to see you cry!'

Her answering smile was as breathtaking as sun rising above the sea. With eyes of liquid green she adored his haggard face, igniting a flame deep within his sombre eyes, bringing a curl to the corners of a mouth which only a short while ago had seemed as if it would never smile again.

'Tara!' he groaned, snatching her back into his arms.

Their first kiss of peace was as solemn as the exchanging of vows, as deep as the commitment they felt, as gloriously happy as the future that stretched before them. Then inevitably, passion began to rise, racing fire through their veins, fusing their bodies with a flame of raw desire, an urgent, naked need.

Tara gloried in his possessive embrace like that of a demented man who has groped towards a mirage and is bemused by the fact that it has not eluded him as it had so many times before. In a passion of remorse she pressed her lips against his and felt him tense.

'Red-haired witch!' he groaned. 'How easily you light my fire!'

With his cheek pressed against hers he looked across her shoulder at the room he had many times likened to a cell, a room in which he had paced away many solitary nights—a prisoner of his word. At this moment it possessed everything he had yearned for—a willing bride, privacy in which to protect her shyness, and a bed on which to allay the intolerable ache a violent need to possess had imposed upon his loins.

But it would not do! The torture he had endured within its walls was too fresh in his mind to be banished to memory.

She suffered a pang of hurt apprehension when suddenly he pushed her away.

'Get dressed,' he urged, 'and hurry!'

'Why ...?' she stammered.

Unable to bear the hurt in her eyes, he pulled her back into his arms and with his lips against her ear he murmured. 'Because, my sweet, enchanting Calypso, your place is in the room I designed especially to suit the nymph that I knew one day would come to me. I am taking you back to Gozo. There we can be together—just the two of us—on our isle of love.'

She did not contradict him. These moments were too precious to be shared. She would wait until later, when they were cradled in each other's arms listening to the pounding of the sea against the rocky shore, before telling him about the life they had conceived within that very room.

She smiled to herself, reminded that the night was calm, the sea rustling like silk against the shore. It did not matter. She and Falcon would be together, weathering their own private tempest—indoors.

The Warrender Saga

The most frequently requested series of Harlequin Romances . . . Mary Burchell's Warrender Saga

A Song Begins	The Curtain Rises
The Broken Wing	Song Cycle
Child of Music	Music of the Heart
Unbidden Melody	
Remembered Serenade	
When Love Is Blind	

Each complete novel is set in the exciting world of
music and opera, spanning the years from the
meeting of Oscar and Anthea in *A Song Begins* to
his knighthood in *Remembered Serenade*. These
nine captivating love stories introduce you to a cast
of characters as vivid, interesting and delightful as
the glittering, exotic locations. From the tranquil
English countryside to the capitals of Europe—
London, Paris, Amsterdam—the Warrender Saga
will sweep you along in an unforgettable journey of
drama, excitement and romance.

The Warrender Saga

The most frequently requested Harlequin Romance series

Complete and mail this coupon today!

Harlequin Reader Service

In U.S.A.
MPO Box 707
Niagara Falls, NY 14302

In Canada
Harlequin Reader Service
Stratford, Ontario N5A 6W2

Please send me the following editions of The Warrender Saga.
I am enclosing my check or money order for $1.25 per novel
ordered, plus 49¢ to cover postage and handling.

☐ 980 A Song Begins
☐ 1100 The Broken Wing
☐ 1244 When Love Is Blind
☐ 1405 The Curtain Rises
☐ 1508 Child of Music
☐ 1587 Music of the Heart
☐ 1767 Unbidden Melody
☐ 1834 Song Cycle
☐ 1936 Remembered Serenade

BONUS OFFER — *We Followed Our Stars*, Mary Burchell's
moving autobiography, is yours ABSOLUTELY FREE when
you purchase all nine Warrender Saga novels.
☐ Yes, I have purchased all nine of the above. Please send me
my copy of *We Followed Our Stars*.

Number of novels checked _____ @ $1.25 each = $ _____

We Followed Our Stars
Mary Burchell's autobiography _____ x $1.50 $ _____

Postage and handling $ _____.49

New York State and New Jersey residents please
add appropriate sales tax $ _____

                       TOTAL $ _____

NAME _____
(Please Print)
ADDRESS _____

CITY _____

STATE/PROV _____ ZIP/POSTAL CODE _____

OFFER EXPIRES JUNE 30, 1979

AB ROM 2264